Introduction

'If Cervantes had never been born,' wrote the Spanish critic Marcelino Menéndez y Pelayo, '*La Celestina*' – here called by its traditional English title, *The Spanish Bawd* – 'would be the greatest imaginative work produced in Spain'*; and our contemporary Gerald Brenan, in his bold and invigorating *Literature of the Spanish People*,† makes an even higher claim for this single production of the Spanish-Jewish lawyer, Fernando de Rojas. Placing it above all other Spanish prose works prior to the middle of the nineteenth century, he affirms that 'it is not only the first European novel but one of the greatest'.

Though written in bare dramatic form, *La Celestina* is certainly a novel. Its length would clearly have prevented stage representation. Indeed such performances as have been mounted in recent years in Spain, Mexico, France, the U.S.A., and England have been so radically cut as to present only single aspects of this many-sided work. For long it was forgotten that classical drama had been written to be acted, and much learned drama of the Middle Ages was written solely for reading. *La Celestina* is in the Latin tradition of Plautus and Terence. Indeed the names of its characters are lightly Castilianized forms of Latin names, some of which occur in their comedies. What is gained by the use of uninterrupted dialogue is a condensation, such as we find again in contemporary novelists like Henry Green. There is no description of places or situations, which arbitrarily change. Everything is conveyed

* *Origines de la novela*, III (Edición nacional de las obras, XV, p. 393).

† Cambridge University Press, 1951 (reprinted by Penguin Books, 1963), Chapter 17.

by conversation, stifled asides, and soliloquy. Yet we know the faces and dress of the characters, and even the lay-out of the city – which was modelled on Salamanca or, possibly, Toledo – in which 'the wiles of a procuress' and 'the lies of their wicked servants' sent 'a pair of crazy lovers' to their doom.

The form and authorship of *La Celestina* present abundant problems that have delighted the more persistent scholars of the last decade or so, in Britain, Spain, France, and the U.S.A. To read them, one would suppose that Rojas had invented mystifications, solely to give them material for theses and learned articles. The first question, to which there is no certain solution, is whether the author of Acts 2 to 21 was also responsible for Act 1, which he claimed in the introduction to the second edition of 1500 to have found in an anonymous manuscript and to have completed in a fortnight's vacation. According to his story, this first act was undivided and unsigned. Finding in it wit, philosophy, and a moral, he felt compelled to fill in the rest, even though this was outside the scope of his profession. He did not say whether the future action had been sketched out by the original author, but threw out a couple of famous names – Juan de Mena and Rodrigo Cota – to whom, he observed, it was generally attributed. Many small touches, invisible in translation, point to the greater antiquity of the first act, which may well have been intended as an interlude, complete in itself. Its subject was not the loves of Calisto and Melibea which gave the completed book its title – at least in the edition of 1500, the first of 1499 lacking a title-page – but the seduction of Parmeno, the faithful servant, by the wicked Celestina. Though the book at present reads like the work of one man, continuing straight from the initial meeting of the lovers to Pleberio's lament for his daughter's death in Act 21, one must not forget that the final work, as we find it in the edition of 1502 and as it is here translated, is longer by five acts than the work published

THE PENGUIN CLASSICS
FOUNDER EDITOR (1944–64): E. V. RIEU
PRESENT EDITORS:
Betty Radice and Robert Baldick
L142

FERNANDO DE ROJAS

The Spanish Bawd

LA CELESTINA

Being the Tragi-Comedy of Calisto and Melibea

TRANSLATED WITH
AN INTRODUCTION BY
J. M. COHEN

PENGUIN BOOKS
BALTIMORE · MARYLAND

Penguin Books Ltd, Harmondsworth, Middlesex, England
Penguin Books Inc., 3300 Clipper Mill Road, Baltimore 11, Md, U.S.A.
Penguin Books Pty Ltd, Ringwood, Victoria, Australia

—

This translation first published 1964

—

—

Made and printed in Great Britain
by C. Nicholls & Company Ltd
Set in Monotype Garamond

TO

PHIL AND VAL

Contents

originally and anonymously by Rojas, who first revealed his name in an acrostic poem prefaced to the edition of 1500. This expansion is wholly justified, since by prolonging the love-affair from one night to a couple of months, it allows Rojas greatly to develop Melibea's character, to present her parents more fully, and to show her gradually yielding to the infatuation, not just swept away by Calisto's urgent wooing. In the book's final form the new acts were numbered 15 to 19, the end of Act 14 was rewritten, since Calisto, instead of dying, was now made to return home, and the end of Act 14 was transferred to the end of Act 19. Acts 15 and 16 therefore became 20 and 21. There are also many retouches throughout, though Act 1 was left almost untouched, a possible proof that Rojas had taken over another man's work, which he did not care to rewrite.

There is no doubt that the additions of 1502 were by Rojas. Since he was a sufficient master of small-scale change successfully to incorporate his various small interpolations, it is perhaps not unreasonable to assume that he was capable of adapting himself still further and imitating another man's style. That his reading differed from that of the author of Act 1 can be judged by the different character of his quotations. In one further respect, he gives unwitting support to his story of dual authorship. How is it, one may ask, that Calisto is able to walk into Melibea's garden in the first scene of Act 1, although he needs a ladder to scale its walls in Act 14? It seems likely that the 'favourable spot' of the original meeting was a church, and that Rojas, misreading the reference to a straying falcon in the second scene, supposed that Calisto had met Melibea when pursuing this bird. Moreover, on the basis of linguistic analyses conducted by Señor Criado de Val, it is reasonable to conclude that the one-act 'Auto' or interlude is a quarter of a century older than Rojas' first expansion of fifteen acts, which he probably made, though perhaps not in a fortnight, only a little while before publication. The attribution of Act 1 to Rodrigo Cota, author of several verse satires, though unproven, is plausible. Like Rojas a converted Jew, he died about 1470.

The second major question is Rojas' general intention. Was he, as he claimed, writing a moral story in order to correct the crazy extravagances of lovers and warn the world against the wiles of procuresses and wicked servants? Or was he, in anticipation of *Romeo and Juliet*, drawing a pair of star-crossed lovers, trapped and destroyed by the intrigues of the bawd Celestina, who played on the weaknesses of servants not originally wicked? Or, to carry the Shakespearean parallel still further, did the lovers' tragedy spring from an implied incompatibility that forbade even the thought of marriage, the logical outcome of their infatuation? It is indeed possible to conclude, on the basis of evidence presented in its fullest form by an unacademic critic, Fernando Garrido Pallardó,* that while Calisto was an Old Christian of pure blood, Melibea, like Rojas himself, was the child of a *converso* family which had, perhaps, even relapsed into Judaism, as did the parents of Rojas' wife. The plain romantic theory of star-crossed love, generally held in the nineteenth century, and this social-religious development, first made in 1957, have aroused the scornful anger of 'Establishment' scholars, who like to think that literature is solely the product of literary influences and has no roots in its authors' feelings or life-experience.† They do not answer Señor Garrido's main points: that the simplicity of Melibea's home, her mother's unpolished language, the ease of Celestina's entrance, Pleberio's failure to protect his

* See *Los problemas de 'Calisto y Melibea'* (Figueras, 1957).

† See my own tentative exposition of Señor Garrido's theory in *The Times Literary Supplement* of 19 June 1959, and letters on 3, 10, and 17 July. Also references in Marcel Bataillon: *La Célestine selon Fernando de Rojas* (Paris, 1961).

daughter or to invoke the Christian God when deploring her death, and the nature of his fortune, which was founded on shipbuilding, all sustain the theory of their Jewish descent and perhaps of their crypto-Judaism, while Calisto's arrogance towards Melibea, the hasty crudity of his lust, and his servants' fear lest his honour suffer from his having died in what would be a ghetto garden, point to the rash young man's superior descent. The theory is far from established, but can perhaps be accepted in part. The best test lies in the reading of the novel. If the idea of racial untouchability heightens the drama, then it can be, at least provisionally, accepted. I am myself impressed by the lack of Christian language in the speeches of Melibea and her father, and by the caddish presentation of Calisto, by turns verbose and lecherous, a very credible portrait of a member of a superior race, seen by an inferior who prides himself on his greater culture, industry, and family feeling. It is difficult to suppose that at a moment when the Inquisition was pursuing all Jews of doubtful orthodoxy, a writer of the suspected minority could write a masterpiece which entirely ignored the plight of the community to which he belonged.

If we accept any part of Señor Garrido's theory, we have to admit that Rojas was at pains to disguise his intention from his less informed readers. Hence his several references to the nobility of Melibea's family, even though their fortune, to which her father frequently refers, was founded on building and trade, not on the possession of landed estates. The anonymity of the work's original publication and its timid acknowledgement, first in an acrostic and then more openly by word of mouth, testify to a certain nervousness in the author. Blasphemy and anti-clericalism occur throughout the work, though with no greater frequency, at least in respect to the latter, than in many works of the late Middle Ages. However, an erring author of impure blood was exposed to particular dangers in the Spain of Ferdinand and Isabella and Charles V. Santa Teresa herself was at greater pains to defend her orthodoxy than she might have been if not of partially Jewish descent; and the authorship of several important works of humanist tinge was unacknowledged. The only contemporary novel comparable in value to the *Celestina*, the rogue-story *Lazarillo de Tormes*, remains anonymous to this day, as does the ironic miscellany *El Crotalón* (*The Timbrel*), which lay in manuscript till the present century. The authorship of the ironic travel dialogues *El viaje de Turquía* (*The Turkey Voyage*), which was also unprinted until recent times, has only lately been established. The risks of authorship in Renaissance Spain were far from negligible.

A third question of lesser importance that has been discussed at some length is the degree of Rojas' belief in witchcraft. Are Celestina's spells to be taken seriously, or were they, as Parmeno suggests when describing her prowess to Calisto in the first act, 'all mockery and deceit'? Certainly she appears to believe that she has summoned the devil into the thread that she takes to Pleberio's house, and that it is he who has sent Melibea's mother away in a hurry, leaving her free to make her first approaches to the girl. Celestina was alone when she called on the fiend, and so could not have been doing it to impress anyone. Perhaps the answer is that the author of the first act intended her witchcraft to be a pretence, but Rojas developed her satanic character. Belief in witchcraft was common at the time, and invocations similar to Celestina's can be found in accounts of trials before the Inquisition.* Moreover Rojas expanded the original picture of the bawd in other respects. Her bibulous conviviality, her delight in lechery, and the ease with which, until the last fatal moment

* See quotation from S. Cirac Estopañán: *Los procesos de hechicerías en la Inquisición de Castilla la Nueva* (Madrid, 1942) in the prologue to Martín de Riquer's edition of *La Celestina y Lazarillos* (Barcelona, 1959), pp. 62–3.

when her greed destroys her, she plays on the weaknesses of masters and servants alike, are Rojas' own contributions to the making of one of the great characters of world literature.

It is not surprising that the book first entitled the *Comedy*, then the *Tragi-Comedy of Calisto and Melibea* soon came to be called by her name, the *Celestina*. The bawd is a sempiternal figure of Spanish literature. She appeared as Trotaconventos in the Archpriest of Hita's poetic miscellany *El libro de buen amor* (*The Book of Good Love*), in which she obtained for the narrator the favours of Doña Endrina, a rich and attractive widow. There are hints for her character in the anti-feminist stories of the Archpriest of Talavera, and Cervantes invented at least one comparable procuress in his 'Exemplary Novel', *La tía fingida* (*The Pretended Aunt*). But Celestina is the greatest, a figure of Falstaffian proportions, infinitely guileful and in the end almost lovable if only for her abounding zest. The other servants are less attractive. Sempronio is a calculating creature and Parmeno, whatever his original good intentions, is speedily corrupted. Moreover both are cowards. Of the women, Areusa, although a whore, has integrity, and at least loves Parmeno disinterestedly. But these servants are there only to point Rojas' moral. They are characterless creatures, rich only in their conversation, which draws, as it would not in life, on all the resources of language from the learned to the colloquial. Melibea's parents are presented as solid, respectable, and affectionate people, deeply devoted to their daughter. But Alisa, at least, unless we are to believe her helpless in the hands of the devil Celestina has invoked, was extremely foolish to leave her daughter with the old bawd, whose character she very well knew. As for Pleberio, though his lament is perhaps the stiffest piece of writing in the book, his miserable fate rouses our pity, left as he is with all his useless wealth, having lost his sole treasure, Melibea. The characters of the lovers are more enigmatic. Perhaps youth provides some excuse for Calisto. He was only twenty-three when he fell to his doom. But the greed with which he demands Melibea's virginity at their first interview, his selfishness in thinking only of his own risk of disgrace when he learns of his servants' execution, and the extravagant impatience of his behaviour when he fears he may be crossed in love, prove him no Romeo. Perhaps he is little more than the exemplary figure of the crazy lover against whom Rojas claims to be warning his readers. The green-eyed Melibea seems to have more individuality. But perhaps it is only the description of her beauty and the shadows of the garden in which she waits for her lover that lend her romantic charm. For if we believe in the reality of Celestina's pact with the devil, she is a mere puppet, more slowly roused than Calisto but as devoid of true feeling. To yield and to kill herself were in that case her inevitable fate, and her sole wrong was that of justifying herself for deceiving her parents and ending her life. She was no more mistress of her actions than Iseult when she had taken the love-philtre. Indeed, it is possible that the characters of Calisto and Melibea are the creation of modern readers, nourished on legends of romantic love, and that for Rojas they were just exemplary figures.

There is no hope of resolving all the questions raised by this very great book. Perhaps we should enjoy it less were we to know all the answers. Yet one final problem – already touched on – must be mentioned, since it has exercised so many critics in the last hundred years. Why, they have asked, did Melibea assume from the start that Calisto's advances were 'illicit'? Why could he not have asked Pleberio for his daughter's hand in marriage? If we accept the theory of untouchability the answer is plain. If we do not, we may fall back on Rojas' statement that his novel is a warning against crazy lovers and their appetites, and observe that the wickedness of unbridled passion was a literary commonplace of the Middle

Ages. Then the book becomes, as the drier modern critics suppose it, merely a consummate variation on a well-worn theme. There could have been no question of marriage, since this would have defeated the author's purpose. My own belief is that what started as a moral tale grew and altered in that supposed fortnight of its composition, till in the end it expressed much that was drawn, perhaps only half-intentionally, from the author's experience both of love and social inferiority.

The *Celestina* achieved a great and immediate popularity. Its medium – the novel in dialogue – was adapted by a number of later authors in Spain and Portugal, the most important of whom was Lope de Vega, whose *La Dorotea*, written towards the end of his life, dramatized a critical love-affair of his youth. Translations into French, Italian, and Latin quickly appeared. The first adaptation in English was an anonymous verse interlude, which appears to have emanated from the circle of Sir Thomas More. The first full translation was made by James Mabbe in 1631. It is a racy work in the best translators' tradition of the age, that is to say somewhat free, and a great deal less spare in its language than the original. There are records of plays on the subject licensed in 1580 and 1598, but these do not survive. The next complete version was by Phyllis Hartnoll (Everyman's Library, 1959). A translation of the sixteen acts of 1500 by Lesley Byrd Simpson appeared in the U.S.A. in 1955.

The present version has been made from the edition of M. Criado de Val and G. D. Trotter (Madrid, 1958). A few emendations have been accepted from various sources in places, particularly in the first act, where the printed lines fail to make sense. In the interests of present-day readers, the linguistic formality of some speeches, especially by Calisto, has been toned down. Verbal extravagance was less tiresome in Rojas' time than it seems now. However, I have left nothing out, merely broken down some sustained extravagances into brief sentences, less apostrophic than those of the original and free of *thee* and *thou*. The best account of the book and its times in English is to be found in Chapter 6 of Gerald Brenan's history, referred to on page 9.

J.M.C.

London, June 1963

THERE FOLLOWS

The Comedy or Tragi-Comedy of Calisto and Melibea

composed as a lesson for those crazy lovers who are so carried away by their unruly passions that they worship their mistresses as divinities, also as a warning against the wiles of procuresses and the lies of wicked servants.

ARGUMENT OF THE WORK

Calisto, a youth of noble family, intelligent, good-mannered, well-bred, and plentifully endowed with talents though of moderate fortune, falls in love with Melibea, an honourable young lady of pure blood, high rank, and great wealth, the sole heir of her father Pleberio and the favourite of her mother Alisa. Her chaste resistance is overcome by Calisto's urgent passion, seconded by the efforts of a wicked and crafty old woman called Celestina and two of his servants whom she has suborned by the promise of pleasure and profit. The lovers and their accomplices come to a bitter and disastrous end.

The tale begins with an unlucky accident which brings Calisto into the presence of Melibea, whom he desires.

The Following Characters appear in this Tragi-Comedy

CALISTO: a youth in love
MELIBEA: the daughter of Pleberio
PLEBERIO: her father
ALISA: her mother
CELESTINA: a procuress
PARMENO, SEMPRONIO, TRISTAN, SOSIA: Calisto's servants
CRITO: a lecher
LUCRECIA: Melibea's maid
ELICIA, AREUSA: loose women
CENTURIO: a pimp

Act One

Calisto enters a garden in pursuit of his falcon, and there finds Melibea, with whom he is deeply in love. He begins to address her, but is sternly dismissed, and returns home very sad. He confides in Sempronio, one of his servants, who with some difficulty persuades him to enlist the help of an old woman called Celestina, in whose house lives Sempronio's mistress Elicia. When Sempronio arrives there on his master's errand, the girl is entertaining Crito, another of her lovers, who is quickly concealed. While Celestina and Sempronio are negotiating, Calisto talks to Parmeno, another of his servants; and their conversation lasts until Sempronio returns with Celestina. The old woman recognizes Parmeno, and tells him at some length of his mother's character and exploits. She persuades him to make friends with Sempronio.

CALISTO: In this I see God's greatness at work.
MELIBEA: In what, Calisto?
CALISTO: In that he has empowered nature to endow you with perfect beauty, and granted me the undeserved favour of finding you in this favourable spot where I can at last declare my secret passion. I have prayed and sacrificed to him, and I have performed pious works, all in the hope that he would grant me this opportunity. But the reward is a thousand times greater than my deserts. Was ever living man so blessed as I am now? The saints in their glory cannot know such joy as I feel in conversing with you. But alas, how unlike them we are! Being pure, they rejoice without fear of falling from their happy state. But I, a creature of matter and spirit, even as I rejoice, fear the tortures I shall suffer when you are gone.

MELIBEA: So you think of this as a great reward, Calisto?

CALISTO: So great that if God were to seat me above his saints in heaven, I should count it a lesser felicity.

MELIBEA: I shall reward you yet more fittingly if you go on.

CALISTO: How blessed are my unworthy ears to hear that promise!

MELIBEA: Not blessed but cursed, you'll say when you've heard me out. I'll make you regret your audacity. This speech of yours is true to your character, and has only one purpose, to dishonour me. But on virtue like mine your words are wasted. Go away, you wretch! Go away! It is intolerable that any man should dare to make wicked advances to me.

CALISTO: I will go as one pursued by cruel fate with special hatred.

*

CALISTO: Sempronio! Sempronio! Sempronio! Where is the wretched fellow?

SEMPRONIO: Here, sir, grooming the horses.

CALISTO: The horses? Why did you come from the hall then?

SEMPRONIO: Your falcon flew home, and I went to put him back on his perch.

CALISTO: The devil take you! May you fall down dead! May you suffer horrible tortures for all eternity! May you meet a worse fate than the painful death that I'm expecting to die! Get along, get along, you scoundrel. Prepare my room and make my bed.

SEMPRONIO: It shall be done, sir, immediately.

CALISTO: Close the shutters. Darkness shall be companion to my grief, and blindness to my misfortune. My sad thoughts are unfit for the light. How happy is the death that comes when it is desired! If the physician Erasistratus were alive he would understand my disease. May Seleucus in his mercy touch Pleberio's heart, so that my lost spirit shall not be sent to join the luckless Pyramus and Thisbe without hope of salvation.*

SEMPRONIO: What does this mean?

CALISTO: Away you fool, and stop talking. Leave me, or my hand will strike you dead before your time.

SEMPRONIO: I'll go, then, if you want to suffer alone.

CALISTO: Go, and the devil go with you!

SEMPRONIO (*to himself*): I don't see how he could go with me seeing that he's staying here with you. Heavens above! Some disaster must have happened. What can it be that has taken this man's spirits away so suddenly? And what's worse, his wits as well. Shall I leave him, or go in to him? If I leave him he'll kill himself, and if I go in he'll kill me. I'll not interfere. It's not my concern. Better for him to die if life's such a burden to him, than for me, who enjoy mine. If I'd no other pleasures except visiting Elicia, that would be reason enough for keeping out of danger. But supposing he kills himself and there's no witness, I shall be held answerable for his death. I'd better go in. But even if I do he won't take comfort or advice. They say it's a bad sign when a man doesn't want to get well. I'd better give him a little time to cool down, all the same. They say it's dangerous to squeeze a boil while it's still hard. It only makes it more inflamed. He can wait a bit then. If a man's in pain we leave him to weep, for tears and sighs are a great relief to a grieving heart. Besides, if I do go in it'll only make him more furious. For the sun burns hottest when it has something to reflect its rays. If the eye has nothing to rest on it

* This very obscure passage is explained by reference to the historian Valerius Maximus, who tells how the physician Erasistratus discovered that Antiochus was sick with love, and persuaded Seleucus to give the young man his daughter. Calisto hopes that Melibea's father Pleberio may be persuaded to act in the same way.

grows tired, but when there's an object near the sight grows keen. So I'd better wait a bit. If he kills himself in the meantime, well, let him die! Perhaps I may pick up something of his that no one else knows about, and so improve my condition. But it's wicked to count on benefits from another man's death. Perhaps this is a temptation of the devil. But if he dies, they may execute me. Then Jack will follow his master. What's more, philosophers say that it's a great comfort in affliction to have someone to listen to one's troubles. A wound's more dangerous, they say, when it's concealed. So in this awkward situation the best thing to do is to go in and patiently console him. Men sometimes recover without physic or doctor, but care and physic make the cure easier.

CALISTO: Sempronio!

SEMPRONIO: Sir?

CALISTO: Bring me my lute.

SEMPRONIO: Here it is, sir.

CALISTO (*sings*): Can any grief compare
With what I bear?

SEMPRONIO: The lute's out of tune.

CALISTO: How can a man tune it who is himself out of tune? What sense of harmony can he have who is himself full of discords? A man whose will refuses to obey his reason, who has barbs in his breast, in whom peace and war, love and hate, injury, guilt, and suspicions battle together? Here, take the lute and sing me the saddest song you know.

SEMPRONIO (*sings*):

Nero watched burning Rome
From the Tarpeian cliff:
The cries of young and old
Caused him no grief.

CALISTO: My fire burns fiercer, and the girl I spoke of has less mercy than Nero.

SEMPRONIO (*aside*): This master of mine is mad, and no mistake.

CALISTO: What are you muttering, Sempronio?

SEMPRONIO: I didn't speak, sir.

CALISTO: Tell me what you said. Don't be afraid.

SEMPRONIO: I was saying, how can the fire that burns one human being be greater than one that devours a whole city and a multitude of people?

CALISTO: How? I'll tell you. A fire that lasts for eighty years is greater than one that is over in a day, and a fire that destroys a single soul is greater than one that burns a hundred thousand bodies. There's as much difference between the fire you sing of and the one that burns me as between appearance and reality, or a painting and a living thing. Indeed if purgatory is like this, I would rather my soul perished with the beasts than attain to the glory of the saints by such a road.

SEMPRONIO (*aside*): I wasn't far wrong. Matters aren't going to stop here. This is not only madness, but heresy too.

CALISTO: Didn't I tell you, Sempronio, to speak up when you talk? What did you say?

SEMPRONIO: I said, God forbid that should be. It's a sort of heresy you were speaking.

CALISTO: Why?

SEMPRONIO: Because what you said was right against the Christian faith.

CALISTO: What has that to do with me?

SEMPRONIO: Aren't you a Christian then?

CALISTO: I'm a Melibean. I worship Melibea, I believe in Melibea, and I love Melibea.

SEMPRONIO (*aside*): Have it your own way. Melibea's so big then that my master's heart can't contain her and she comes spilling out of his mouth. But I've heard enough. (*Aloud*) I know where the trouble lies and I'll cure you.

CALISTO: You're promising the impossible.

SEMPRONIO: On the contrary, it's quite easy. Once the doctor recognizes the disease, the cure's begun.

CALISTO: What advice can put right something that has been wrong from the start?

SEMPRONIO (*aside*): Ha, ha, ha! So this is the fire that burns Calisto! So this is his trouble, is it? Does he imagine he's the first that love has struck with a dart? Almighty God, how mysterious are your ways! You've made love very powerful, that it should drive a lover crazy like this. You've given it an ample territory, yet lovers always find it too narrow. Like young bulls that feel the goad, they break out in a wild charge and leap the barriers headlong. You commanded man to forsake mother and father for his wife. But he does more. Like Calisto here, he abandons you and your law as well. But I'm not surprised. Philosophers, saints and prophets, they've all forgotten you when they are in love.

CALISTO: It's wrong to deceive when you're painting a moral. Don't you glory in praising your mistress Elicia?

SEMPRONIO: Follow my good advice, not my bad example.

CALISTO: What are you scolding me for?

SEMPRONIO: For submitting your masculine dignity to the imperfections of a weak woman.

CALISTO: A woman, you lout? A goddess, a goddess!

SEMPRONIO: And you believe that? Or are you joking?

CALISTO: How should I be joking? I believe her to be a goddess, I proclaim her a goddess and, although she dwells on earth, I say there's no other sovereign in heaven.

SEMPRONIO: Ha, ha, ha! (*Aside*) Did you ever hear such blasphemy? Did you ever see such blindness?

CALISTO: Why are you laughing?

SEMPRONIO: Because I never thought till now that there was a worse sin than the one invented in Sodom.

CALISTO: Explain yourself.

SEMPRONIO: Well, the Sodomites tried to commit abominations with angels in disguise, but you have picked one whom you claim to be a goddess.

CALISTO: Damn you if you haven't made me laugh, which I hadn't expected to do this year.

SEMPRONIO: Come now! Were you going to weep for the rest of your life?

CALISTO: Yes.

SEMPRONIO: Why?

CALISTO: Because I feel too unworthy to approach the woman I love.

SEMPRONIO (*aside*): You cowardly son of a bitch! Remember Nimrod, remember Alexander the Great. They thought themselves worthy not only to rule this world but heaven too!

CALISTO: I didn't quite catch what you said. Say it again before you go on.

SEMPRONIO: I said, do you, who have more courage than Nimrod or Alexander, despair of approaching a woman, when many women of high rank have submitted themselves to the foul-breathed embraces of low muleteers, and to brute beasts? Haven't you read about Pasiphae and the bull? Or about Minerva and Vulcan?

CALISTO: Those are old wives' tales. I don't believe them.

SEMPRONIO: Was that business of your grandmother and the ape an old wives' tale? Your cuckold of a grandfather will stand witness.

CALISTO: Curse this fool! What rubbish he talks!

SEMPRONIO: So that touched you? Read the histories, study the philosophers, examine the poets. The books are full of tales about wicked women, and the sad ends that men like you have come to for believing in them. Listen to Solomon, who says that women and wine make men deny God. Consult Seneca, and see what he thinks of them. Hear

Aristotle, look at St Bernard. Gentiles and Jews, Christians and Moors, all are in agreement here. But you mustn't make the mistake of believing that what I have said applies to the whole sex. There have been and are many saintly, virtuous, and noble women, whose shining crowns exempt them from the general obloquy. But as for the rest, no one could tell you the whole story of their lies, plots, fickleness, desires, tempers, and effronteries. Once they get an idea into their heads, they don't hesitate. They'll take any risk. And what about their dissimulations, gossipings, deceits, and forgetfulnesses? What about their antipathies, ingratitudes, and inconstancy, their affirmations and denials and prevarications, their presumption, boastfulness, and mock-humility, their folly, scorn, pride, servility, loquacity, and greed, their filthy lusts, their cowardice, their insolence, sorcery, impostures, gibes, and scoldings, their shameless-ness and their panderings? Consider how little brain there is beneath their broad and delicate hoods. What thoughts go on inside those gorgets, under all their finery and their long, stately gowns! What cess pools of corruption lie behind those painted temples! Truly they have been called limbs of Satan, fountain-heads of sin, destroyers of Paradise. Have you not read the passage for St John's day, 'This is woman, the ancient curse that drove Adam from the delights of Paradise. She it was that consigned the human race to hell; she it was that was rebuked by the prophet Elijah', and so on?

CALISTO: Tell me now, didn't they all – Adam and Solomon and David and Aristotle and Virgil and every other man you've mentioned – fall a prey to women? And am I stronger than they? And how do you know all this? Who were your teachers?

SEMPRONIO: Why, women, of course. Once they reveal themselves to you they lose all shame and let you see all this and more besides. But you must live up to your position as a man of honour, and try to surpass even your own estimate of yourself. It's better for a man to aim above his merits than to fall from the place where he rightly belongs.

CALISTO: But how does this apply to me?

SEMPRONIO: I'll tell you. Firstly, you're a man with a good intellect. Secondly, nature has endowed you with her finest gifts: good looks, charm, well-shaped limbs, strength, and agility. Then, fortune has given you such a liberal share of her goods that your outward qualities are as resplendent as your inward. Isn't this true? Without worldly goods, of which Fortune's the mistress, no one in this life was ever called happy. But it's your fate to be universally loved as well.

CALISTO: By all except Melibea. And in every quality for which you have praised me, Sempronio, Melibea is incomparably and immeasurably my superior. Consider the nobility and antiquity of her lineage, her vast wealth, her most excellent intelligence, her resplendent virtues, her stature and ineffable grace, and her supreme beauty – of which I beg you to let me speak a little, for it will afford me some relief. And I shall speak only of her visible beauties, for if I could describe those that are hidden, there would be no need for us to hold this miserable conversation.

SEMPRONIO (*aside*): What nonsense will this wretched master of mine bring out now?

CALISTO: What did you say?

SEMPRONIO: I said, go on, I shall be delighted to listen. (*Aside*) And if I do enjoy your speech, may God reward you!

CALISTO: What?

SEMPRONIO: I said I shall enjoy your speech, and may God reward you for it!

CALISTO: Well then, for your pleasure, I'll draw her portrait in more detail.

SEMPRONIO (*aside*): Here's trouble coming! See what I've let myself in for! But tiresome though it is, it will have an end.

CALISTO: I will begin with her hair. Have you ever seen that fine gold thread which they spin in Arabia? It's lovelier than that, and just as bright, and reaches to the very soles of her feet. But when it's parted, and tied with one of those fine ribbons, which is how she wears it, it is enough to turn men to stone.

SEMPRONIO (*aside*) Into donkeys, you mean.

CALISTO: What did you say?

SEMPRONIO: I said, very different from a donkey's.

CALISTO: What a comparison! You're a fool.

SEMPRONIO (*aside*): Well, how sane are you?

CALISTO: Her eyes are large and green, her lashes long, her brow shapely and high, her nose delicate, her mouth small, her teeth little and white, her lips full and red, her face oval, her bosom high, and as for the full firmness of her little breasts – who could describe it? How it will rouse a man to see them! Her skin is smooth and lustrous; her complexion would make the snow look dark, and her colour could not be more pink and white if she had chosen it for herself.

SEMPRONIO (*aside*): There's no stopping this fool.

CALISTO: Her hands are small, but not too small, and their flesh is smooth. Her fingers are long, and her nails pointed and so pink that they look like rubies set in pearls. And those parts that I have not seen are, to judge by their outward shape, incomparably more beautiful than those of that goddess whom Paris pronounced the most beautiful of the three.

SEMPRONIO: Have you finished?

CALISTO: I have been as brief as I could.

SEMPRONIO: Even if every word you say is true, you as a man are worth more than she.

CALISTO: How's that?

SEMPRONIO: Because she's imperfect, and for that reason desires and lusts after you, and after others inferior to you. Haven't you read what the philosopher* says, that as matter desires form so woman desires man?

CALISTO: But alas, when shall I see Melibea desire me?

SEMPRONIO: It's a possibility. And you might come to loathe her too just as much as you love her now. For once you possessed her, you'd see her with different eyes, free of your present illusions.

CALISTO: With what eyes?

SEMPRONIO: With clear eyes.

CALISTO: With what eyes do I see her now?

SEMPRONIO: With eyes that magnify, so that a little seems a lot and what's small appears great. However, to save you from despair, I'll deal with this matter and get you what you desire.

CALISTO: Oh, God grant you your dearest wishes! It's good to hear you speak like this, though I don't expect you'll succeed.

SEMPRONIO: I certainly shall.

CALISTO: God bless you, Sempronio. That brocaded doublet I wore yesterday is yours. Take it and wear it.

SEMPRONIO: God reward you for this – (*aside*) and for the other gifts you'll be giving me. There'll be plenty of them. Indeed, I'm doing pretty well, and if he offers many more inducements like this I'll bring her straight to his bed. It's the doublet that does it, for no one can work well without pay.

CALISTO: Now don't you be idle.

SEMPRONIO: Nor you either. A good servant can't work for a lazy master.

CALISTO: How do you mean to set about this good work?

SEMPRONIO: I'll tell you. A little while ago I met on the edge

* Aristotle.

of the town an old bearded body called Celestina. She's a crafty witch up to every kind of wickedness. They tell me that here, in this city, more than five thousand maidenheads have been broken and repaired under her auspices. She can move the hardest rocks, and tempt them to lechery if she has a mind to.

CALISTO: Could I talk to her?

SEMPRONIO: I'll bring her to you here. Make up your mind to be gracious to her and liberal with your presents and, while I'm gone, think out the best way to tell her your troubles. She'll find you a good remedy for them.

CALISTO: What are you waiting for?

SEMPRONIO: I'm just going. God be with you!

CALISTO: And with you too! O almighty and eternal God, guide of those who stray, you who brought the Orient kings to Bethlehem, following a star, and led them back to their own country, I humbly entreat you to guide my Sempronio, so that he may turn my pain and sorrow into gladness, and I, though unworthy, may attain my desires!

*

CELESTINA: Good news, good news, Elicia! It's Sempronio, Sempronio's come.

ELICIA: Sh! Sh!

CELESTINA: What's the matter?

ELICIA: I've got Crito with me.

CELESTINA: Quickly! Push him into the broom-cupboard. Tell him your cousin's coming, a dear friend of mine.

ELICIA: Hide in here, Crito. My cousin's just come.

CRITO: All right. I'll hide. Don't you worry.

SEMPRONIO: Blessed mother, how I've longed to see you! Thank God I've found you here.

CELESTINA: My son! My big son! What a fright you gave

me! I can't get my breath. Come and give me another kiss. It must be three days since you've been to see us. . . . Elicia, Elicia, see who's here!

ELICIA: Who, Mother?

CELESTINA: Sempronio.

ELICIA: Oh, dear, dear, how my heart does pound!

CELESTINA: Here he is. Come and see him. But I'll have his kisses. He shan't give them to you.

ELICIA: Oh, you damned rogue! May you be eaten by sores! I'd like to see your enemies kill you. I'd like to see the pitiless law hang you for all your wicked crimes.

SEMPRONIO: Ho, ho! What's the matter with my Elicia? What's upsetting you?

ELICIA: Three days without coming to see me! May God never look on you again! A poor fool I've been to put my trust and all my hopes in you.

SEMPRONIO: Hush, dearest. Do you suppose distance has the power to quench my heart's love or to extinguish the fire in my breast? You are always with me wherever I go. Don't upset yourself, or give me worse tortures than I've suffered already. But tell me, whose step is that upstairs?

ELICIA: What? Oh, it's one of my lovers.

SEMPRONIO: I don't believe you.

ELICIA: It's true, I swear. Go up and see for yourself.

SEMPRONIO: Very well, I will.

CELESTINA: Come come, don't take any notice of her. She's all moods. She's so upset by your neglect that she's gone crazy now you're here. Come and talk to me. Don't let's waste the chance.

SEMPRONIO: Well, who is it upstairs?

CELESTINA: Do you want to know?

SEMPRONIO: Yes, I do.

CELESTINA: A girl who was sent to me by a friar.

SEMPRONIO: What friar?

CELESTINA: Don't be inquisitive.

SEMPRONIO: But tell me, mother, what friar?

CELESTINA: Well, if you insist. The rector . . . the fat one.

SEMPRONIO: Oh, poor girl, what a load she's got to bear!

CELESTINA: We all bear them. But you haven't seen many of us with saddle-sores.

SEMPRONIO: Not saddle-sores, but swollen bellies.

CELESTINA: Oh, you're a wit.

SEMPRONIO: Never mind that. Let me see her.

ELICIA: Ha, you nasty fellow! So you'd like to see her, would you? Your eyes are starting out of your head. One woman isn't enough for you, eh? All right, go and see her, but you'll have seen the last of me.

SEMPRONIO: Be quiet, for goodness sake. What are you getting excited about? I don't want to see the girl, or any other girl either. I want to talk to our mother. Leave us alone, please.

ELICIA: Oh, you ungrateful beast! Go away, go away and stay away for another three years, if you like.

SEMPRONIO: Now, Mother, you must trust me. You know I wouldn't deceive you. So pick up your cloak and out we go. I've got something to tell you that will be useful to you and to me too. But we must be quick. I'll explain to you on the way.

CELESTINA: Very well, let's go. Good-bye, Elicia. Lock the door after us – and good-bye, house! I'll be back soon.

SEMPRONIO: Now, Mother dear, put every other thought out of your head, and listen carefully to what I am going to say. Don't let your mind wander, for if you think of several things at once you don't pay proper attention to anything. And if you do strike the truth it's only by accident. But, first of all, let me say something I've never told you before. Eves since I came to trust you, I've always meant, if I were to strike lucky, to share my luck with you.

CELESTINA: If God were to give you a half share in his Kingdom it would be no more than you deserve for your kindness to this old sinner. But don't keep me waiting. Tell me your story. We've been friends for too long now to stand in need of preambles and introductions and beatings-about-the-bush. Cut them short and come to the point. What's the use of a lot of words when a few will do?

SEMPRONIO: Very well. Calisto is mad with love for Melibea. He needs your help and mine. And since he needs us both, we can both make a good thing out of it. To recognize an opportunity and seize it is the sure way to prosperity.

CELESTINA: That was well put. I catch your drift. You don't have to tell me anything twice. This is good news, as the surgeon says when they tell him a man has cracked his skull. He begins by probing the wound, so as to raise the price of his treatment. And I'll do the same to Calisto. I'll make him doubt his cure. For hope deferred, as they say, makes the heart sick. And the more hopeless he gets, the bigger his longing will be. You understand me, eh?

SEMPRONIO: That's enough. Here we are at his door, and walls, as they say, have ears.

*

CELESTINA: Knock then.

Sempronio does so.

CALISTO: Parmeno!

PARMENO: Sir!

CALISTO: Damn you, man, are you deaf?

PARMENO: What is it, sir?

CALISTO: Someone's knocking at the door. Run.

PARMENO: Who's there?

SEMPRONIO: Open the door, Parmeno. It's I, Sempronio, with a lady.

PARMENO: Sir, it's Sempronio with an old painted bawd that's making all that noise.

CALISTO: Be quiet, you wretch. The lady's my aunt. Hurry and open the door. (*Aside*) I might have known. You only escape one danger to fall into a worse one. By concealing this business from Parmeno, who's bound to me by love or loyalty or fear, I've offended the old lady, who has more power over my life than God himself.

PARMENO: What's worrying you, sir? What's the trouble? D'you suppose she'll take the name I called her as an insult? Don't you believe it! She's just as pleased to be called by it as you are when they call you a true gentleman. Besides, it's her proper title. Everyone knows she's a bawd. If she's in a crowd, and some woman calls out, 'Hullo, old bawd!', she'll turn round without the least embarrassment and answer with a smile. That's what they call her at parties, feasts, weddings, brotherhoods, burials, and every other festivity. If a dog sees her, he barks, 'Old bawd!' Birds sing it, sheep bleat it, and donkeys bray it as she goes by. The frogs in the marshes croak it, and if she enters a smithy the hammers beat it out. Carpenters, armourers, farriers, tinkers, and fullers, all make the air ring with the name. Joiners sing it, carders and weavers beat time to it, and farmers in their fields, at the plough, in the vineyard or at the harvest, lighten their daily labours with the sound. You can hear her praise ring out whenever a gambler loses his stake. Everything that has a voice calls her by name as she goes by. And her husband was a great hawker of boiled eggs.* What more can I say, except that when one stone strikes another, it cries out, 'Old bawd!'

CALISTO: And how do you come to know all this?

PARMENO: I'll tell you. Many years ago my poor mother was a neighbour of this Celestina, and the old lady borrowed

* Probably a term for a cuckold.

me from her as her servant. She doesn't recognize me now, because I didn't serve her for long. Besides I've changed a great deal now that I'm grown up.

CALISTO: What kind of work did you do for her?

PARMENO: I went with her to market and carried her provisions and kept her company and did anything else I had the strength for. In the little time I was with her I learnt a thing or two that I haven't forgotten after all these years. The good lady had a house on the edge of the town. It stands a bit back from the road, near the tanneries and beside the river. It is a tumbledown place, in poor repair and badly furnished. She had six trades in all. She was a seamstress, a perfumer, a master hand at making up cosmetics and patching maidenheads, a procuress, and a bit of a witch. Her first trade was a cover for the rest. It gave young servant-girls an excuse for visiting her house, to be repaired and at the same time to sew shirts and ruffs and other such things. When they came, they would bring a piece of bacon, or some wheat or flour, or a jug of wine, or any other sort of provisions they could steal from their mistresses, and even greater thefts were covered up there. She was a great friend of students, stewards, and priests' servants. And she'd sell them the flesh of these poor innocents, who took the risk lightly, relying on her promise to patch them up. But she didn't stop at that. She used these girls as a means of approach to the most carefully guarded young ladies, with whom she conducted similar business. Under cover of such solemn events as Stations of the Cross, nocturnal processions, midnight and early masses, and various private devotions, I've seen many such enter her house with their faces muffled, and followed by heavily disguised penitents, barefoot and with their breeches unlaced, who went in to weep for their sins! You can guess the trade she carried on. She physicked babies and collected flax at one house to be spun at another – as an excuse for entering them all. It was 'Mother, come here!' and 'Mother, go there!' or 'Where's the old lady!' or 'Here comes the mistress!' Every woman knew her. But despite all her activities, she never missed mass or vespers, or neglected the monasteries and nunneries, where she practised her tricks and intrigues. At home she distilled perfumes out of concoctions of storax, benzoin, myrrh, animé, ambergris, civet, powders, musk, and musk-rose. She had a room full of retorts and flasks and different-shaped vessels, made of earthenware, glass, tin, and brass. She made corrosive sublimate, boiled and silvered cosmetics, face-paint, lip-salve, lotions, unguents, lustres, polishers, clarifiers, and whitening. And she concocted other cosmetics from powdered asphodel, senna, snakeroot, gall, sour grapes, and new wine, distilled and sweetened with sugar. For softening the skin she used lemon juice, turpeth, deer and heron marrow, and other confections. She manufactured toilet waters from roses, orange-blossom, jasmine, clover, honeysuckle, carnation, and reseda, powdered and soaked in wine. She made hair-bleaches from vine-shoots, bog-oak, rye, and horehound, mixed with saltpetre, alum, yarrow, and various other ingredients. She extracted oils and fats from the carcasses of cows, bears, horses, camels, snakes, rabbits, whales, heron, bittern, chamois, wild cats, squirrels, hedgehogs, and otters. It would be tiresome to list them all. And it was a sight to see the herbs and roots she used for her lotions hanging from the ceiling of her room. There was camomile, rosemary, mallow, maidenhair fern, melilot, elderflower, mustard, lavender, white laurel, bindweed and couch-grass, wild pink and liverwort, golden rod and leaf-scarlet. You would never believe what face-washes she distilled from storax, jasmine, lemon, melon-seed, violets, benzoin, pistachio-nuts, pinekernels, grape-pips, jujube, fennel, lucerne, vetch, sunspurge, and chickweed. And she always carried a little balsam in a flask, to rub into that sore she has on her nose. As for maidenheads, some she repaired with bladders and others with a few stitches. She kept a stock of fine furrier's needles and waxed silk thread in a little painted box on her shelf; and hanging from it were roots of spikenard and red sumach, squill and cardoons, with which she worked marvels. Why, when the French ambassador was here, she sold one of her girls three times over as a virgin.

CALISTO: She could have done it a hundred!

PARMENO: By God, you're right! Orphans would come to her and other girls who had gone wrong, and these she mended for nothing. In another room she kept philtres to cure and arouse love, made from stags' hearts, vipers' tongues, quails' heads, asses' brains, foals' and babies' cauls, string-beans, loadstone, hangman's rope, ivy flower, hedgehogs' bristles, badgers' feet, fern seed, stones from eagles' nests, and any number of other things. She was visited by plenty of people, both men and women. Some of them she would ask for a piece of bread they had bitten, or a garment, or a lock of hair. Or she would paint letters on their palms in saffron or vermilion, or give them wax hearts stuck full of broken needles, or ugly things made of clay or lead. She would draw figures on the ground and recite spells. I couldn't tell you all the things that old woman did. And it was all nothing but mockery and deceit.

CALISTO: That's enough, Parmeno. Leave the rest for another time. You've warned me and I'm grateful for it. But we mustn't stay here, for necessity brooks no delay. We asked the old lady to come, and we've kept her waiting too long. Let's go, or she may get cross. I am afraid, and fear clouds the memory but sharpens the foresight. Hurry now, let's get to work. But one thing I beg of you, Parmeno. Don't let your envy of Sempronio prevent the remedy on which my life depends. He's serving me well in this business. And if I gave him a doublet, you shall certainly have a coat. Don't imagine I value your information and advice any less than his practical efforts. For the spiritual outweighs the temporal, as I very well know. Although animals work harder than men, they are merely fed and tended, but never regarded as friends. There lies the difference between my feelings for Sempronio and for you. Let me tell you in private that, though I remain your master, I look on you as a friend.

PARMENO: I'm sorry you should doubt my loyalty, sir, and think I need admonitions and promises to give you proper service. When did you see me envious, sir, or placing my interests and comforts before your welfare?

CALISTO: Don't take offence, Parmeno. Your breeding and behaviour put you first in my eyes, before all my other servants. I promise you that. But this is a difficult business, and my whole life and happiness depend on it. I have to be careful and foresee every contingency. Of course I know that good manners bespeak a good character. But a good character may be a matter of artifice. . . . Still, enough of this. Let's go and see the physician.

*

CELESTINA: I hear footsteps. They're coming downstairs, Sempronio. But pretend you don't hear them. Listen now, and for the benefit of us both let me do the talking.

SEMPRONIO: By all means.

CELESTINA: Now, don't pester me with your importunities. All this insistence is like flogging a willing horse. You take your master's troubles as hard as if you had changed places with him, and both of you were suffering the same torments. But believe me, I haven't come here without a remedy. I'll win his suit for him, or die in the attempt.

*

CALISTO: Stop a moment, Parmeno, and listen to what they're saying. Let's see how we stand. What a marvel of a woman! No gifts on earth could justly reward her noble spirit! And faithful, honest Sempronio! Did you see, Parmeno? Did you hear? Aren't I right? What do you say, dear friend and counsellor, dear keeper of my secret soul?

PARMENO: Sir, having protested my innocence of the crime you suspect me of, I will, in all due loyalty, give you my opinion. Listen to me, and don't let passion dull your ears, or hope of pleasure blind your eyes. Be calm and unhurried. For some are so eager to score a bull that they miss the target. I may be young, but I've seen many things in my time; and seeing many things is what you call experience. Those two either saw you or heard you coming down the stairs, and that is the reason for this cunning conversation, on which you're counting to get what you desire.

SEMPRONIO: I don't like the tone of Parmeno's voice, Celestina.

CELESTINA: Don't worry. As true as I'm alive, where the ass goes the saddle will follow. Leave Parmeno to me, and I'll win him over. We'll give him a share of what we gain. For there's no joy in sitting on a fortune. We'll all make a profit, we'll all take a share, and we'll all be happy together. I'll bring him to you so tame and gentle that he'll eat out of your hand. We'll make him a partner in this, and, as they say, three shall ride the donkey.

*

CALISTO: Sempronio!

SEMPRONIO: Sir?

CALISTO: What are you doing? Key to my life, open the door! O, Parmeno, she's here at last! And I'm alive and well again. Oh, what a dignified, venerable old lady! You'll generally find, Parmeno, that you can judge the inward qualities by the physiognomy. O virtuous age! O aged virtue! Here is my hope of gaining my desire! Here my desire has gained its dearest hope! Here's the relief of my suffering, the end of my tortures, my regeneration, the renewal of my life, and my resurrection from the dead! Let me embrace you and kiss those healing hands, but, alas, I am unworthy. From this moment I worship the ground you tread on, and kiss it reverently.

CELESTINA: I don't live on fine speeches, Sempronio. Does your fool of a master imagine he can feed me with these old chewed bones? That's not my opinion, as he will see in due course. Tell him to shut his mouth and open his purse, because I don't trust his deeds, let alone his words. I'll give you fine words, my noble ass. You didn't get up early enough to fool me.

PARMENO (*aside*): I don't like the sound of this. If the master's in trouble, the man'll catch it too. Here's poor, unlucky, blind Calisto kneeling down to worship the most ancient and whorish piece of clay that was ever beaten round the brothels. He's destroyed, he's conquered, he's fallen beyond redemption, help, or counsel.

CALISTO: What was our mother saying, Sempronio? I gather that she thinks I was offering her words instead of a tangible reward.

SEMPRONIO: I gathered the same myself.

CALISTO: Then come with me and bring the keys, and I'll put her mind at rest.

SEMPRONIO: That's a good plan. Let's go at once. For you

mustn't let tares grow among the wheat, or suspicion in the heart of a friend. Weeds must be rooted out with the hoe of good deeds.

CALISTO: You're talking sense. Let's go, and quickly.

*

CELESTINA: I'm glad to have this chance, Parmeno, of telling you that I love you. You have a place in my heart, you know, little though you deserve it, I say this because I overheard what you were saying just now. But I don't mind that. Virtue bids us suffer provocations, and not repay evil with evil, especially when we are provoked by mere boys who haven't learnt the lessons of the world, and let their silly loyalty ruin both themselves and their masters, as you are ruining yourself and Calisto. I heard you well enough. Don't imagine I've lost my hearing in my old age, or my other senses either. Not only can I hear and see and understand, but with my mind's eye I can penetrate to the root of things. You realize, of course, Parmeno, that your master's suffering from lovesickness. But don't let that make you think he's a weakling. For love's invincible. It sweeps everything before it. Let me tell you, if you don't know it already, that two things are certain in this world: men and women must love one another, and when a man's truly in love passion sweeps him away. For love is a sovereign delight, ordained by the universal Creator for the perpetuation of the human race, and without it mankind would perish. And not only mankind, for fish, animals, birds, and reptiles are endowed with the capacity to love; and even some plants feel this attraction when they are placed together with nothing between them. Herbalists and farmers indeed believe that they are male and female too. What do you say to that, Parmeno, my little fool, my little simpleton, my little pet, my little treasure, my silly little donkey? Are you grimacing at me? Come here, you young rogue. You know nothing of the world and its pleasures. But I'll be damned if I'll have you anywhere near me, old though I am! Your voice is beginning to break, the down's blossoming on your cheeks, and I'll bet the prick that hangs between your legs doesn't give you much peace.

PARMENO: It's like a scorpion's tail.

CELESTINA: Or worse. A scorpion's sting hurts, but it doesn't cause a swelling. But yours starts a swelling that lasts for nine months.

PARMENO: He, he, he!

CELESTINA: Does that make you laugh, you randy rascal?

PARMENO: That's enough, Mother. Don't scold me, and don't think I'm a fool, even though I am young. I love Calisto because I'm grateful to him. He has always looked after me, and he has always been generous to me. He has treated me well and honourably too, which makes me even more beholden to him. For a servant's love depends on his master's kindness, and without it there's no such thing. Calisto seems a lost man to me, for there's nothing worse than to pursue something without hope of ever getting it. Especially since he's relying on the useless advice and fatuous arguments of that creature Sempronio to bring this very difficult business off. Why, that's like trying to extract crab lice with a shovel and hoe. It's more than I can bear. It brings tears to my eyes even to speak of it.

CELESTINA: But can't you see, Parmeno, that it's plain stupidity to cry over something that tears won't help?

PARMENO: That's why I'm crying. Because if tears could possibly help my master, I should be so pleased that I should be far too happy to cry. But as things are, I can't see any hope. Therefore I'm sad, and can't help crying.

CELESTINA: Then you're crying to no purpose, for something you can't prevent or cure by shedding tears. Has this thing never happened to other people, Parmeno?

PARMENO: Yes, but I don't like to see my master suffering.

CELESTINA: He isn't suffering really, and even if he were he could be cured.

PARMENO: What you say doesn't convince me because, as the logicians say, in good things the fact counts for more than the possibility, and in evil the possibility for more than the fact. So it is better to be well than to be curable, and it's worse to be in danger of illness than actually to catch a disease. In sickness, the possibility is worse than the event.

CELESTINA: I don't understand what you're talking about, you young villain. You're not suffering like your master, are you? Then what's all this long rigmarole about? What are you complaining of? But have your little joke if you want to, and turn the truth upside down, and believe whatever you like. The fact is the man's sick, and the possibility of curing him lies in the hands of this weak old woman.

PARMENO: This weak old whore, you mean.

CELESTINA: May God strike you dead, you young villain! How dare you...!

PARMENO: But I know you.

CELESTINA: Who are you?

PARMENO: I'm Parmeno, the son of your old friend Alberto. My mother sent me to you once, and I was your servant for a month when you lived on the river bank near the tanneries.

CELESTINA: Good gracious me! So you're Claudina's son Parmeno, are you?

PARMENO: I certainly am.

CELESTINA: Well may St Anthony burn you with his fire! But your mother was just as much of an old whore as I am. So what have you got against me, Parmeno my boy? Oh yes, you're Parmeno all right. Come to me now, come right over here. Lord, the beatings and whippings I've given you in my time. And the kisses too. Do you remember when you used to sleep at the end of my bed, you little rascal?

PARMENO: Yes, I do indeed. And sometimes you used to pull me up on the pillow and squeeze me against you, although I was only a child. But I used to run away because you smelt old.

CELESTINA: May you die of the pox! How dare you say such a thing? But enough of this nonsense. Listen to me, my boy, and pay careful attention. They called me here for one purpose, but I came for another. Although I pretended at first that I didn't know you, it was you I really came to see. You remember, Parmeno, that when your mother, God rest her soul, left you with me, your father was still alive. Well after you ran away from me, the poor man died of grief. The last years of his life were very sad, because he was always worrying about your disappearance, and wondering whether you were still alive. Now on his death-bed he sent for me and privately put you in my charge, with no other witness between us but he who witnesses all our acts and thoughts and examines the very depths of our hearts. He made me swear before God that I would search for you and find you, and give you a home; and then, when you were a man and capable of living a steady life, I was to tell you where he had hidden a great store of gold and silver, worth more than the whole of your master Calisto's fortune. And because I gave him my word and he died happy, and because a promise made to the dead is more sacred than one made to the living – for the dead can't act for themselves – I spent a great deal of time and money searching for you, until it pleased him who bears all our burdens, and listens to our just prayers, and directs all our pious endeavours, that I should discover you were here, which I did only three days ago. It used to make me very sad, I promise you, to think of you wandering about the world, with nothing in your pocket, and no friends or relatives to look after you. For, as Seneca tells us, wanderers have many lodgings but few friends, since they do not stay anywhere long enough to make good ones. A man who lives in many places belongs nowhere. Food can't nourish the body if it's thrown up as soon as eaten. What's more, there's nothing so bad for the health as perpetual changes of diet. A wound never heals if it's treated with many ointments, and a plant never thrives if it's always being transplanted. There is nothing so beneficial that its effect is instantaneous. Therefore, my son, give up your youthful follies. Take your elders' advice and return to reason. Find something to rely on. And what could be more reliable than my kindness, my love, my counsel, to which your parents entrusted you? Now let me tell you, as your true mother, on pain of the curse which your parents laid on you should you disobey me, that for a while you must put up with your present master and serve him, until such time as I advise you otherwise. But don't be stupidly loyal. Don't put your trust in him, for masters today are shifty and changeable. Make friends for yourself, for friends are dependable, and be loyal to them. You can't live on air. So it's no use trusting the empty words of gentlemen, who waste their servants' substance with hollow promises. They suck your blood like leeches. They're inconsiderate, they abuse you, they forget your services, and then refuse to pay you.

It's a poor look-out to grow old in a palace. As was written of the pool of Bethesda, of a hundred who enter only one is cured. Masters today love themselves better than their servants, and come to no harm by it. But servants should put themselves first too. Favours, generosity, and noble deeds are things of the past. Every master captures his servant's affection and then abuses it. Well, servants, being in the subordinate position, should follow their example, and obey the same rule. I say this, Parmeno my boy, because I think this master of yours is a skinflint. He wants everyone to serve him, but gives nothing in return. Keep your eyes open and you'll see that I'm right. Make friends for yourself in his household, for friends are the most precious things in the world. But expect no friendship from him, for it seldom exists between men of different rank and fortune. We have a matter in hand, as you know, by which we can all make a profit, and by which you can at this moment improve your position. As for the other thing I told you about, that can wait till the time is ripe. But you'll do yourself a lot of good if you'll make friends with Sempronio.

PARMENO: What you say makes me tremble, Celestina. I don't know what to do. I'm all confused. On the one side, I think of you as my mother; on the other, of Calisto as my master. I want to be rich, but the man who uses foul means to climb is more likely to tumble than reach the top. I don't want ill-gotten gains.

CELESTINA: Well I do. I'm for gains by fair means or foul.

PARMENO: I shouldn't be happy with ill-gotten gains. There's something decent about being poor and contented. Besides, it isn't those who have little that are poor, but those whose desires are great. So, whatever you say, I don't trust you in this. I want to live my life free of envy, to cross deserts and rough places unafraid, to sleep without waking in a fright, to be able to answer if I'm accused, to be able to fight back, and to resist all oppression.

CELESTINA: How true it is, my boy, that wisdom only comes with old age! You are very young.

PARMENO: If a man's poor and humble, then at least he's secure.

CELESTINA: Come, say with Virgil that Fortune favours the brave. But no matter what a man's fortune, he won't want to live without friends. Worldly well-being you have, thank God, and you must realize that if you're to keep it you need friends. But don't imagine the favour of that master of yours will keep you safe, because the more you are favoured the less safe you are. That's why in difficult times your only recourse is to your friends. And is there any better person to choose as a friend than one who can offer all three kinds of friendship: for mutual improvement, for profit, and for pleasure? As for the first, Sempronio's character is very much like your own and you have many virtues in common. As for profit, you've only to come to an agreement with him, and the profit's yours; as for pleasure, you would get that too, since at your age you're keen for every kind of amusement, much more so than we who are too old. I mean sports and masquerades and jokes, and eating and drinking and love-affairs, all enjoyed together. If only you would agree, Parmeno, what a wonderful life we should have together! Sempronio is in love with Elicia, Areusa's cousin.

PARMENO: Areusa's?

CELESTINA: Yes, Areusa's.

PARMENO: Eliso's daughter Areusa?

CELESTINA: Yes, Eliso's her father.

PARMENO: Are you sure?

CELESTINA: Yes, quite sure.

PARMENO: That's marvellous.

CELESTINA: Are you pleased then?

PARMENO: Nothing could please me better.

CELESTINA: Well, you're in luck, for here's the woman who can get her for you.

PARMENO: O Mother, I can't believe anyone any more.

CELESTINA: It's rash to believe everyone, but foolish to believe no one.

PARMENO: Of course I believe *you,* Mother, but I don't dare . . . Please go away.

CELESTINA: Oh, you poor creature! It's a faint heart that can't take good news. God gives no meat till a man has lost his teeth. What a simpleton you are! I suppose you think you've only to be wise and you won't need any help from Fortune, and that the shrewder you are the less you depend on luck. Those are old wives' tales.

PARMENO: But, Celestina, I've heard my elders say that an example of lechery or avarice is very harmful, and that a man must associate with people who improve him and avoid those he'll need to improve. Now Sempronio's example won't improve me, and I shan't cure him of his vices. So even if I felt like following your advice, I should prefer to be secret about it. I should want to keep my sins hidden, so as not to set a bad example. A man may act wrongly out of wickedness, but he should not violate decency.

CELESTINA: You talk like a fool. You can't enjoy anything alone. Don't be sour and unsociable, for Nature detests gloom and strives for pleasure. It's pleasant to share your delights with your friends, and especially to recount and discuss your love-affairs. 'That's what I did – That's what she said – This is how we played – This is how I took her – This is how I kissed her – She bit me so – and then I embraced her – and then she gave in. Such talk and gaiety and sport and kisses! Let's go there! Let's go back! Let's have some music. Let's make up rhymes. Let's sing catches, tell riddles, play at competitions. What device shall we begin with, or what letter? There she goes to mass. She'll come out again tomorrow. Let's stroll down her street. Here's a note she sent me. Let's go there at night! Hold the ladder for me. You wait at the door. What luck did you have? See the old cuckold, he's left her alone. Let's try again, let's pay her another visit.' Ah, Parmeno, can a man enjoy all this without company? The true enjoyment lies in the company, believe me, I know. That's the real pleasure. As for the other thing, the donkeys in the field can do it better than we can.

PARMENO: I don't mean to let you convince me, Mother, that these things are good just because they're pleasant. You're like one of those preachers who for lack of sound arguments introduce the sweet poison of heresy to fascinate and captivate the minds of the weak, and blind the eyes of reason with the sweet dust of desire.

CELESTINA: What's reason, fool? And what's desire, ass? Nothing will teach you that except the discrimination you haven't got. And better than discrimination is prudence, which can only come with experience. And experience only comes with age. That's why you call old people like me Mother and Father. And good mothers and fathers give their children good advice as I'm giving it to you, for I value your life and honour far above my own. And when will you repay me for all this? Never. Parents and masters never get their just reward.

PARMENO: But I'm very much afraid of getting bad advice, Mother.

CELESTINA: So you won't listen? I'll tell you what Solomon said: The man who is so stiff-necked as to despise his teacher will come to a sudden and violent end, and health will not be in him. I've finished with you, Parmeno, and with this whole business.

PARMENO (*aside*): Now I've annoyed the old lady. But I'm doubtful about her advice. It's a mistake to believe nothing, and it's wrong to believe everything. Yet it's natural for a man to believe, especially someone who offers to help him, and Celestina's promising me not only profit but love as well. We are told we should trust our elders. Now, what does she advise me to do? Make peace with Sempronio?

One mustn't refuse peace, for blessed are the peacemakers; they shall be called the children of God. And one should not reject love or charity towards one's brothers, and not many refuse profit. So I had better listen to the old woman. (*Aloud*) Look, mother, a teacher shouldn't be cross if a pupil's ignorant, or no one would be taught anything. For learning must be passed from one to another, and you don't find it everywhere. So forgive me and go on with what you were saying. I want to listen to you, and I'll trust you, and what's more I take your advice as a special favour. But please don't thank me. It's the giver not the receiver who deserves praise and thanks for the gift. So tell me your orders, for I'll humbly agree to what you say.

CELESTINA: To err is human, but to persist in error is brutish. So I'm glad, Parmeno, that you've finally wiped the cobwebs from your eyes, and proved yourself a worthy son of your father, who was a very keen, intelligent, and level-headed man. Merely to remember him brings floods of tears to my poor old eyes. I can't help crying, as you see. Like you, he would sometimes cling stubbornly to his principles, but he always acknowledged reason in the end. When I saw the fight you were putting up just now, and then how you came round, I swear to God I might have had him standing before me in the flesh. What a handsome, well-built man he was! And how venerable he looked! But that's enough. Here come Calisto and your new friend Sempronio. You must make your peace with him as soon as you can. For two minds in harmony are stronger both for thought and action.

*

CALISTO: I've been so out of luck lately, Mother, that I was afraid I shouldn't find you alive. But considering all my anxieties, it's even more marvellous that I stand here alive myself. Accept this poor gift from one who offers you his life with it.

CELESTINA: As when purest gold is shaped by the hand of a master craftsman, the object is worth more than the material, so the gracious manner of your exquisite generosity enhances the magnificence of the gift. Indeed, promptness in giving doubles the sum, while tardiness indicates a reluctance to fulfil a promise, or regret at having offered anything at all.

*

PARMENO: What did he give her, Sempronio?

SEMPRONIO: A hundred gold crowns.

PARMENO: Whew!

SEMPRONIO: Did the old lady say anything to you?

PARMENO: Sh! Yes, she did.

SEMPRONIO: Then how do we stand?

PARMENO: As you wish, but I'm scared.

SEMPRONIO (*aside*): I'll make you twice as scared before we've finished.

PARMENO (*aside*): Oh God, there's no plague more deadly than an enemy in one's own house.

*

CALISTO: Go now, Mother, and bring joy to your household. Then come back quickly and bring joy to mine.

CELESTINA: God be with you!

CALISTO: And, if he loves me, with you too.

Act Two

Celestina having gone home, Calisto is left talking with Sempronio. Now that his hopes are excited, he is impatient of every delay. So he sends Sempronio to make sure of Celestina's help in the business he has at heart. Calisto and Parmeno then remain in conversation.

CALISTO'S HOUSE

CALISTO: I gave the old lady a hundred crowns. Was that right, fellows?

SEMPRONIO: Yes, that was right. You've not only found a cure for your troubles, but done yourself great honour as well. For what is the use of fortune's blessings and favour, except to serve honour, which is the greatest of worldly possessions? It is the prize and reward of virtue, and that is why we do honour to God, having nothing better to offer him. Now the better part of honour is liberality or open-handedness. It is tarnished by the amassing of crude worldly goods, but enhanced to the utmost degree by liberality and magnificence. What profit is there in keeping things that bring one no profit? To use wealth is undoubtedly better than to possess it. How glorious it is to give, and how miserable to receive! And as to act is better than to possess, so the giver is nobler than the receiver. Fire, being the most active of the elements, is the noblest, and so occupies the highest place among the spheres. Some say there is merit in nobility that is based on the deeds and lineage of one's ancestors, but I say there is no glory in reflected light, if a man has none himself. Don't pride yourself, therefore, on your father's nobility, though he was a splendid man, but on your own. For this brings you honour, the highest quality a man can gain, and one by which the good, but never the wicked, can worthily attain perfect virtue. And I'll say more, that you can't attain perfect virtue without perfect honour. So be glad that you have been so liberal and open-handed. But now take my advice and go and rest in your room, for your business is in good hands. It's begun well, and therefore you can be sure that it'll end even better. But let's go now for I have a good deal more to say to you about this business.

CALISTO: It seems wrong, Sempronio, that I should stay here in good company while she, who is trying to cure my troubles, is left to her own devices. It would be better if you were to go with her and spur her on, for you know that my well-being depends on her diligence. I shall suffer if she delays; if she forgets I shall despair. You are wise, and I believe you're a good and loyal servant. Go, and let the sight of you remind her of the grief that tortures me, the fire that burns me. I was so distressed that I couldn't explain to her a third part of my secret malady; my tongue was wild and my senses were bewildered. You, being free from these afflictions, can speak to her quite freely.

SEMPRONIO: I should like to obey you, sir, but I should also like to stay here and comfort you. Your fears urge me on, but your solitary brooding holds me back. The voice of obedience says, Go and hurry the old woman. And I should like to. But how can I? As soon as you're alone, you'll be raving like a madman, sighing and groaning, wailing and lying in the dark, refusing company and seeking new ways of torturing your mind. And if you go on in that way you'll undoubtedly end by dying or going mad, unless you have someone with you all the time to suggest amusements and joke with you, to sing gay songs and recite ballads, to read stories and invent riddles, to make up tales, to play cards or chess – someone, in fact, who can contrive every kind of pastime, and won't let your thoughts wander off into the cruel despair that struck you at your first fatal meeting with your lady.

CALISTO: How silly you are! Don't you know that it relieves suffering to bewail its cause? When you're sad it's very sweet to complain of your passion. Every sigh you heave brings assuagement with it. Sobs and groans reduce the pain, and make it easier to bear. All writers on consolation agree about this.

SEMPRONIO: But turn over the page and read on. You'll find them saying that to trust what is transient, and to pursue things that bring sadness is nothing but a kind of insanity. Remember that idol of all lovers, Mathias, who complained to oblivion that he alone did not forget. The pains of love lie in thinking about it; to forget is to have rest. Now stop kicking against the pricks. Pretend to be happy and easy in your mind, and you will be. For though thought doesn't change the facts, it often influences a situation by moderating our feelings and controlling our judgement.

CALISTO: Since you're reluctant to leave me alone, Sempronio my friend, call Parmeno and let him stay with me. And continue to be as loyal to me as ever, for a servant's loyalty is a master's reward.

PARMENO: Here I am, sir.

CALISTO: But I am absent, I didn't see you. Don't leave her, Sempronio, and don't forget me. God be with you.... Now, Parmeno, what do you think about the events of today? My suffering is great, Melibea is above me, and Celestina is a wise physician with skill in these things. We can't go wrong. Despite your dislike of her, you've confirmed me in my judgement. I believe what you say, for such is the power of truth that it can even command the tongue of an enemy. I accept your account of her, but I would still rather give a hundred crowns to her than five to anyone else.

PARMENO: (*aside*): What, tears already? We're in trouble now. You may be generous, but it's we who'll go short.

CALISTO: Now be kind to me, Parmeno. Tell me your opinion, and don't hang your head when you answer. Jealousy is a sad thing, and sadness is silent. But I'm afraid it may have more power over you than your fear of me. What did you say just then, you tiresome fellow?

PARMENO: I said that your generosity would be better employed in giving presents and doing favours to Melibea than in gifts of money to that old woman whom I know so well. But the worst of it is that now you've put yourself in her power.

CALISTO: What do you mean by in her power, fool?

PARMENO: When you tell someone your secret, your freedom's gone.

CALISTO: There's something in what the fool says. But when there's a great gulf between the wooer and the wooed, let me tell you – either an immense superiority or a difference of rank or wealth – there must be an intermediary. My intermediary must give my message directly to that lady whom I think it is impossible for me to address again. Such being the case, tell me if you approve of my action.

PARMENO (*aside*): I'm damned if I do!

CALISTO: What did you say?

PARMENO: I said that evils never come singly, and that one misfortune opens the door to many more.

CALISTO: I agree with what you say, but I don't see the application.

PARMENO: Well, sir, the other day you lost your falcon, and that was your reason for going into Melibea's garden.

Your going in led to your seeing and speaking to her. Your speaking to her led to love, and love has been the cause of your grief. And your grief will cause you to lose your body, your soul, and all you possess. And what distresses me even more is that you've fallen into the hands of that old procuress, who has been three times tarred and feathered.

CALISTO: Go on, Parmeno. I like it. The more you abuse her the better I'm pleased. They can tar and feather her a fourth time for all I care, so long as she does my business. You have no feelings, Parmeno. It's easy for you to talk. You haven't got a pain in your heart, as I have.

PARMENO: I'd rather have you angry with me, sir, for annoying you, than cursing me afterwards, when you're sorry, for not offering you good advice. You lost your freedom, sir, when you surrendered control of your will.

CALISTO: The rascal's asking for a beating. Tell me, you ill-bred creature, why do you abuse the woman I adore? What do you know of honour? Tell me now, what is the nature of love? Or since you set up as a clever fellow, give me a definition of good breeding. Has no one ever taught you that the first stage of folly is to imagine you have wisdom? If you felt my pain, you'd use a different lotion to bathe this burning wound that Cupid's cruel arrow has dealt me. Sempronio is running to fetch me help, but you're undoing his work with your idle tongue. You pretend to be loyal, but you're just a mass of flattery, a bundle of malice, and the incarnation of jealousy. To defame that old woman at all costs, you call my love into question, though you know very well that this pain of mine, this tempestuous grief, is not subject to reason, has no use for warnings, but is in need of advice. But do not advise me to tear my heart from an object that I could only relinquish with my life. Advise me of some better course. Sempronio was afraid to go and leave me with you. But I insisted, and now I'm suffering from his absence – and your presence. I'd rather be alone than in bad company.

PARMENO: It would be a poor sort of loyalty, sir, that would be turned to flattery by fear of punishment, especially when one's master has been driven out of his natural senses by grief or love. But the veil will fall from your eyes. This momentary passion will pass; and you'll find my harsh words a better cure for this cruel ulcer than Sempronio's soft ones, which keep your love alive. He feeds and quickens the fires, fans the flame, and throws on fresh fuel, which will destroy you utterly, and bring you to the grave.

CALISTO: Be quiet, you wretch, that's enough. You philosophize while I'm in tortures. It's more than I can stand. Have one of my horses brought out and thoroughly groomed, and see that his girths are well tightened, in case I ride past the house of my lady and goddess!

PARMENO: Boys! Isn't there a groom in the house? Then I shall have to do it myself. (*Aside*) I shall soon come down to worse things than grooming a horse. Come, let's get along with it. Nobody likes to hear the truth. Are you whinnying, master stallion? Isn't one randy beast enough in a house? Or . . . can you scent Melibea too?

CALISTO: Isn't that horse coming? What are you doing, Parmeno?

PARMENO: Here he is, sir. Sosia has gone out.

CALISTO: Well, hold my stirrup, and open the door wider. And if Sempronio comes back with the old lady, tell them to wait. I shall be back very soon.

PARMENO: May the devil run off with you, and may you never come back! Tell these madmen what it's in their interest to hear and they won't even look you in the face. If he were to get a prick in the heel more brains would leak out, I swear, than he has in his head. All right, Celestina and Sempronio can strip you of your last penny for all I care! I'm out of luck. This is what I get for being loyal. Others are wicked and profit by it. I'm virtuous and it ruins me. That's the way of the world. But since traitors are called wise and loyal men fools, I'll go with the crowd. If I follow Celestina, with her seventy odd years of experience, Calisto will do me no harm. This will teach me how to deal with him in future. If he says, 'Let's eat!' I'll say the same. If he wants to pull down the house, I'll agree. If he wants to burn his possessions, I'll go for a torch. Let him break and destroy, let him smash and spoil, and give his property to procuresses, I'll take my share! There's good fishing in troubled waters, they say. But I'll never be caught like this again.

Act Three

Sempronio follows Celestina home, and reproaches her for being slow. They try to devise a way of bringing Calisto and Melibea together. Finally Elicia comes in, and Celestina departs for Pleberio's, leaving the other two alone in the house.

SCENE ONE: IN THE STREET

SEMPRONIO: How slow the old body is! Her feet were a bit brisker on the way out. But pay in advance, and you'll get poor service. Hey, Madam! Hey, Celestina! You don't seem in much of a hurry.

CELESTINA: What do you want, my son?

SEMPRONIO: It's this patient of ours. He doesn't know what to do with himself. He isn't satisfied with the help he's getting. He's dancing with impatience. He's afraid that you may neglect his business, and he's cursing himself for being close with his money, and not giving you enough.

CELESTINA: It's perfectly natural for lovers to be impatient. Every delay's a torture to them, and they can't bear being put off. They want their schemes carried out in a couple of minutes, and completed before they're begun. This is particularly true of novices, who snatch wildly at every bait, and never think what harm they may be doing themselves or their servants – who have to manage their business – so long as they can satisfy their appetites.

SEMPRONIO: What did you say about their servants? Do you think this affair might land us in trouble? Could the sparks from these fires of Calisto's burn us? Then, to the devil with him – and his love! If there's the slightest snag in this affair, I shall leave his service. It's better to lose your wages than the life to enjoy them. But I'll know what to do when the time comes, because there's bound to be some warning, the way there is with an old house before it collapses. But don't you think we ought to keep out of danger, Mother, and let things take their course? If he doesn't get her this year, maybe he will next, or maybe never. Nothing's so painful that it doesn't become easier and more bearable with time. No wound's so agonizing that time doesn't soothe its sting, and no pleasure's so delightful that it doesn't diminish with the years. Good and evil, prosperity and adversity, joy and sorrow, all lose their intensity with time. We may welcome some new event with surprise and delight, but once it's past it's forgotten. We see or hear something new every day, and every day we pass on, leaving the new thing behind for time to reduce to pettiness and unimportance. You might be astonished by the news of an earthquake or some such disaster, but you'd soon forget it, wouldn't you? The river may freeze over, a blind man may see, your father may die, or a thunderbolt fall, Granada may be captured, the king may arrive today, the Turks may be beaten, there may be an eclipse this morning, the bridge may be swept away, someone may be made bishop, Peter may be robbed, and Inez may hang herself. But do you tell me that three days later, or at the second time of telling, anyone will be surprised? Everything is like that; it happens, it's past, it's forgotten. And this love of my master's will be no different; the longer it continues, the more it will shrink. Familiarity takes the edge off pain and pleasure alike, and makes marvels seem commonplace. So we had better make our profit while he's still excited. If we can help him simply and easily, that will be fine; and if we can't, we may wear down Melibea's fury or scorn little by little. But failing that, it'd be better for the master to suffer than for the servant to risk his neck.

CELESTINA: You're right, I'm with you entirely. If we act as you say we can't go wrong. But all the same, my son, a good lawyer has to put some work into his case. He must invent some arguments, and trump up some evidence. And he must attend the court, even though he gets abused by the judge. It would never do to have people say that he takes his fees and does nothing. If he's active, they'll all bring their suits to him – and their love affairs to Celestina.

SEMPRONIO: Do as you think best. This can't be the first affair that you've undertaken.

CELESTINA: The first, my son! You haven't seen many virgins set up shop in this city, thank God, whose wares I haven't been the first to peddle. Every girl child that's born I write down in my book, just to see how many escape my net. Did you think, Sempronio, that I live on air? What estates have I inherited? Do I own a house or a vineyard? Do you know of any other wealth I possess except my profession that keeps me in food and drink and clothing and shoes? I was born and bred in this city, and I've lived an honourable life, as everybody knows. I'm a person of note, aren't I? If a man can't tell you who I am, then he's a stranger in these parts.

SEMPRONIO: Tell me, Mother, what passed between you and my mate Parmeno when I went up with Calisto for the money.

CELESTINA: I told him the whole story from A to Z, and that he'd do better by joining us than by fawning on his master. I warned him that if he didn't change his mind he'd be poor and despised for the rest of his life. I told him too that it was no good playing the saint to an old dog like me. 'Remember what your mother was,' I said, 'and you won't look down on my trade, because whatever abuse you throw at me will strike her first.'

SEMPRONIO: Have you known him as long as that, Mother?

CELESTINA: I, Celestina, was there at his birth, and it was I that helped to raise him. His mother and I were hand in glove. I learnt all the best tricks of my trade from her. We ate together, we slept side by side, we took our pleasures and amusements together, we consulted together and made our plans together. Indoors and out, we were like two sisters. I never made a penny that I didn't give her half. If I still had her with me, I shouldn't be cheated as I am now. O death, death, you take our dearest companions from us! After your unwelcome visits how many are left disconsolate! For every one whom you devour in season you cut down a thousand before their time. If she were alive, I should not be walking friendless and alone. What a loyal friend and good comrade she was to me, God bless her soul! She never let me do anything alone when she was there. If I brought the bread she brought the meat. If I laid the table she put on the cloth. She was never foolish or fanciful or proud as women are nowadays. She could go barefaced from here to the edge of the city, and I swear to you no one along the road would call her by any worse name than 'Señora Claudina'. And certainly nobody was a better judge of wine or provisions. She would be back from the market before I thought she had got there. She was always welcome there, for all the shopkeepers loved her; and she never came back without eight or ten titbits, and a measure of wine inside her as well as one in her jar. They would let her take two or three gallons at a time with no more fuss than if she had left a silver plate in pledge. Her word was as good as hard cash in every wine-shop. If we felt thirsty when we were in the streets, we would enter the first inn, and she would order a pint to wet our throats. And I promise you no one ever made her leave her bonnet for surety. They would put it on the tally, and on we went. If only her son were like her now, your master would be plucked already, I can tell you, and we should have nothing to complain of. But I'll shape him up if I live. I'll make him toe my line.

SEMPRONIO: But how do you mean to do it? He's a slippery customer.

CELESTINA: Then it'll be a case of Greek meeting Greek. I'll see that he gets Areusa, and he'll be our man. He'll give us the chance then to spread our nets undisturbed for Calisto's gold pieces.

SEMPRONIO: But do you think you can do anything with Melibea? Is there a good way in there?

CELESTINA: No surgeon can judge a wound at the first probing. I'll tell you how I see things at present. Melibea is beautiful, Calisto is crazy and free with his money. Spending won't hurt him, and bustling around won't hurt me. So long as the money rolls in, the business can drag on as long as it likes. Money can do anything; it can break rocks and cross rivers dry-shod. There's no hill so high that an ass with a load of gold can't climb it. His wild passion will be quite enough to ruin him and make our fortunes. That's as much as my nose has told me so far, and as much as I know about him or her. But it's enough for us to make good use of. Now I'm off to Pleberio's. Good-bye.... Melibea may be difficult, by the way, but this won't be the first time, thank God, that I've made a woman stop cackling. They're all ticklish at the start, but once they've taken a saddle on their backs, they never ask for a rest. The whole country lies before them, and they'll go on till they drop. If they're travelling by night, they hope the sun'll never rise, and curse the cocks for announcing the dawn and the clock for going too fast. They turn astrologers, and worship the Pleiades and the pole star. And when they see the morning star in the sky it's as if their souls were leaving their bodies. Its light brings gloom to their hearts. I could never travel enough on that road myself. I never seemed to tire. And even now, old as I am, God knows I'm still willing. And if that's true of me, how much more of those who burn unsatisfied? They're caught at the first embrace. They woo their own wooers. They feel the pangs they once inflicted. They become slaves where once they commanded. They break down walls, open windows, feign sickness, and oil the squeaking hinges of their doors to stop their noise. The first sweet kisses of their lovers transform them completely. Women know no moderation; they swing from one extreme to another.

SEMPRONIO: I don't understand this language of yours, Mother.

CELESTINA: I mean that a woman either adores the man who is wooing her, or else she loathes him. Once she has rejected a man, I mean, she can't control her dislike of him. And knowing all this as I do, I have as much confidence in going to Melibea's as if I held her in the palm of my hand. Of course I know I shall have to plead with her at first, but in the end she'll be pleading with me. She may start by threatening me, but she'll be flattering me later on. I always carry a little thread in my bag, as an excuse for visiting houses where I'm not well known, and a few other trifles as well, things like ruffs, hair-nets, fringes, edging, tweezers, mascara, whitening and sublimate, needles and pins, something for everybody. So wherever I'm sent I'm always well prepared either to bait my traps or make my request point-blank.

SEMPRONIO: Take good care what you're doing, Mother. One false step at the start and you'll come to grief. Think of her father, a brave and noble gentleman, and of her mother, a strict and jealous woman – and of yourself, a most suspicious character! Melibea's their only child; if they lose her they lose everything. It makes me tremble to think of it. I hope you won't go for wool and come back shorn.

CELESTINA: Shorn, my son?

SEMPRONIO: Or feathered, Mother, which is worse.

CELESTINA: Well, I'm sorry I ever had to take you for a partner. Do you imagine you can teach Celestina her trade? Why, I had every tooth in my head before you were born. You'd be a fine one to lead me, with all your fears and suspicions!

SEMPRONIO: You needn't be surprised that I'm frightened, Mother. It's natural enough when you've set your heart on something to be afraid that you may never get it. What's more, in this case I'm afraid for you as well as for myself. I want money, and I hope this business'll come off, not just so as to cure my master of his troubles, but to get myself out of penury as well. That's why, being inexperienced, I see more difficulties than you, who are a past mistress in these matters.

SCENE TWO: CELESTINA'S HOUSE

ELICIA: Well, Sempronio, wonders will never cease! I can hardly believe my eyes. It's something new for you to pay us two visits in one day.

CELESTINA: Oh, be quiet, you fool! Don't tease him. We've got something else on our minds, something much more important. Tell me, is there anyone in the house? Did that girl go who was waiting for the friar?

ELICIA: Yes, there's been another one since, and she's gone too.

CELESTINA: Not without getting what she came for, I hope?

ELICIA: Oh dear no, God forbid! She may have come late, but with God's blessing, better late . . .

CELESTINA: Then run up to the attic over the parlour, and fetch me down that bottle of snake-oil. You'll find it hanging on the piece of rope that I brought in from the fields the other night, when it was very dark and raining. Then open the yarn-box and on the right hand side you'll find a paper written with bat's blood. It's under the wing of that dragon whose claws we drew yesterday. And mind you don't spill the may-dew that I've made up for someone.

ELICIA: It isn't where you said, Mother. You never remember where you put anything.

CELESTINA: Don't scold me, for God's sake, in my old age, and don't bully me, Elicia, or show off because Sempronio's here. And don't get high and mighty either. He'd rather have me to advise him, you know, than you as his mistress, although you love him so dearly. Go into the closet where I keep the ointments, and you'll find it in that black cat's skin, where I told you to put the she-wolf's eyes. Bring down the goat's blood too, and those bits of his whiskers that you cut off.

ELICIA: Here they all are, Mother. Take them. I'm going upstairs with Sempronio.

CELESTINA: I conjure you, melancholy Pluto, lord of the depths of hell, emperor of the court of the damned, proud captain of the fallen angels, master of the sulphurous fires that well from boiling Etna, overseer of the tortures and the tortuers of sinful souls, controller of the three Furies Tisiphone, Megera, and Alecto, administrator of all dark things in the kingdom of Stygia and Dis, with its lakes, infernal shades, and chaos of contentions, chief of the winged harpies and their companions, the hideous and frightful hydras, I, Celestina, your most renowned servant, conjure you by the virtue and force of these scarlet letters; by the blood of this bird of night, with which they are written; by the power of the words and signs that are contained in this paper; by the cruel vipers' venom of which the oil was made with which this thread is anointed; come without delay and obey my command. Wind this thread around you, and do not let it go till the time comes for Melibea to buy it. Then remain so tangled in it that the longer she gazes at it the more inclined she is to grant my request. Lay her heart open, and strike it with such a fierce and strong love for Calisto that she will forget her modesty, reveal herself to me, and reward me for my labours and my message. Once this is done, you may ask and require of me what you will. But if you do not obey me with all speed, I declare myself your mortal enemy. I shall then let the light into your dark and gloomy dungeons, and denounce your continual lies. I shall pour my harshest curses on your hideous name. I conjure you once, twice, and thrice. Now, trusting in my great power, I set out with my thread, in which I trust I carry you entwined.

Act Four

SCENE ONE: IN THE STREET

Celestina walks along, talking to herself, till she reaches Pleberio's door, where she finds his maidservant Lucrecia, with whom she starts a conversation. They are overheard by Alisa, Melibea's mother, who, when she is told who the old lady is, invites her into the house. A message arrives for Alisa, who departs. Celestina is left in the house with Melibea, to whom she reveals the reason for her coming.

CELESTINA: Now that I'm alone I'd better consider what it was that alarmed Sempronio about this errand of mine. For though things may sometimes succeed when they're not properly thought out, more often than not they come to grief. Careful consideration, on the other hand, never fails to bring its reward. Although I didn't admit it to him, it might cost me no less than my life if Melibea's people were to catch me making an approach to her. And even if I were to escape with my life I should come off pretty badly, for they would either toss me in a blanket or give me a cruel whipping. Then that hundred crowns would be hard earned indeed! Oh, dear me, what a noose I've put my neck into! Just to show how keen and busy I am, I've risked my life on a gamble. What is a poor wretched creature to do now? If I withdraw I make no profit, and if I go on I can't help running a risk. Shall I go on or turn back? It's a hard puzzle to decide. I can't think which to choose for the best. Audacity will clearly lead me into danger, but cowardice means loss and disgrace. What happens to the ox that won't plough? Every road has its own clefts and pitfalls. If I'm caught red-handed, I'll be executed for sure, or put in jail at the very least. And if I withdraw, what will Sempronio say? That all my power and knowledge and scheming, my tricks and promises, my keenness and cunning amounted to no more than this. And what will his master Calisto say? What will he do? What will he think? That my ways are full of deceit, and that like the cunning cheat I am I've revealed the plot in order to make a bigger profit out of the other side. And even if this vile thought doesn't occur to him, he'll shout like a madman, and throw vile insults in my face. He'll call me all sorts of bad names for the delays he's suffered because of my sudden change of mind. 'You old whore,' he'll say, 'why did you inflame my passion with your promises? Your feet are at everyone's service, you tricksy old bawd, but only your tongue at mine. You act and cheat for them, but for me you only talk. You cure their troubles, but you only torture me. You labour for others, but you do nothing for me. You bring them light, but leave me in darkness. Tell me, you old traitor, why did you offer me your services? Your promise gave me hope, hope postponed my death, gave me fresh life, and made me a happy man. But since nothing came of it, you won't escape punishment and I shan't escape my hopeless grief.' I am a poor old woman, with danger on both sides of me, and trouble whichever way I turn. But when there's no middle course, it's wise to choose the lesser evil. I'd rather offend Pleberio than annoy Calisto. I shall go then. For the shame of skulking like a coward is worse than any punishment I can get for boldly keeping my promise. Fortune never failed the brave. Now here I am at the door. I've been in worse fixes than this. Courage, Celestina, courage! Don't lose heart. There are always lawyers who'll get you off the worst. And the omens look good, if I know anything of these matters. Three of the four men I've passed on the way are called Juan, and two of them are cuckolds. The first word I heard in the street was on the subject of love. And I didn't stumble as I usually do. The very stones seem to open and make way for me to pass. My skirts don't hinder me, and I don't feel tired from walking. Everybody's greeting me. No dog has barked at me, and I haven't seen a blackbird or thrush or raven or any other bird of ill-luck. And best of all, here is Lucrecia at Melibea's door. Being Elicia's cousin, she won't work against me.

SCENE TWO: PLEBERIO'S HOUSE

LUCRECIA: Who can this old woman be who is coming in such a hurry?

CELESTINA: Peace be on this house!

LUCRECIA: Celestina, dear Mother, I'm glad to see you. What lucky chance has brought you into these unlikely parts?

CELESTINA: Love, my dear girl, and the wish to see you. I've brought you a word from Elicia, and I want to see your two ladies as well, the old one and the young one, because I haven't paid them a visit since I moved to the other side of the town.

LUCRECIA: Was that your only reason for coming? You amaze me. You don't usually stir from your house unless there's some profit in it.

CELESTINA: What can be more profitable, silly, than to do what you like? All the same, since we old women are always in need, and especially I who have other people's daughters to support, I've brought a bit of yarn to sell.

LUCRECIA: Didn't I say so? I'm not so silly after all. You never stick your finger in anywhere without bringing out a plum. It happens that my mistress, the older one, is weaving a piece of cloth. So she needs thread, just as you need to sell it. Come in and wait, and you'll be able to do some business.

ALISA: Who's that you're talking to, Lucrecia?

LUCRECIA: The old woman with the scar on her face, madam, the one who used to live near the tanneries, down by the river.

ALISA: That doesn't mean anything to me. What's the good of explaining one mystery by making another? It's a waste of time.

LUCRECIA: Good gracious, madam, but everybody knows the old lady! Surely you haven't forgotten how they put her in the stocks as a witch, and for selling girls to the priests and ruining hundreds of married women?

ALISA: What's her trade now? Perhaps I shall know her better by that.

LUCRECIA: She's a perfumer, madam, and makes whitening, and has thirty other trades. She's very clever with herbs and she physics babies, and some people call her the old charm-seller.

ALISA: I don't recognize her by anything you've said. Tell me her name, if you know it.

LUCRECIA: If I know it, madam! Why there's no one, old or young, in the whole city who doesn't know it. How can I help knowing it?

ALISA: Why don't you say it then?

LUCRECIA: I'm ashamed to.

ALISA: Come say it, you fool. Be quick or I shall lose my temper.

LUCRECIA: Her name's Celestina, madam, begging your pardon.

ALISA: Ha, ha, ha! The devil take you if I can help laughing! You must hate that old woman very bitterly if you're ashamed even to mention her name. I'm beginning to remember her now. A fine old baggage! She must have come to beg for something. Tell her to come up.

LUCRECIA: Come up, Aunt.

CELESTINA: God's grace be with you and your noble daughter, dear lady! I've been too sick and troubled to visit you before, as I should have done. But God knows I had the intention, and the love as well. Distance doesn't dim the love in an old woman's heart. I've been longing to see you, and now my needs have brought me. On top of all my other troubles, I've got short of money, and the best remedy I could think of was to sell a bit of yarn that I was keeping by me to make veils of. I heard from your maid that you needed some. Although I'm poor and God has forgotten me, here it is, very much at your service, as I am myself.

ALISA: I'm touched by your kind thought, dear neighbour, and also by your offer. I'd gladly help you in your need without taking your thread. But I would be grateful for it, and if it's as good as you say, I'll pay you well for it.

CELESTINA: Good, lady? May my life and old age be as good as this thread, and yours too, madam, God bless you! It's as fine as the hair on your head, and as strong as a fiddle-string, and as white as a snowflake, and all spun, reeled, and wound by these fingers. Look, here it is, in little skeins. They gave me threepence an ounce for it yesterday, as I hope to be saved.

ALISA: Let this honest old body stay with you, Melibea darling. It's time I went to visit my sister – Cremes' wife, you know. I haven't seen her since yesterday and she's just sent her page to say that her illness got worse some hours ago.

CELESTINA (*aside*): The devil's been busy hereabouts. He's made the sister worse to provide me with an opportunity. Well, don't let go, old friend. Now's my chance! Hang on tight, and take this person out of my way!

ALISA: What were you saying, my dear?

CELESTINA: I was cursing the devil and my bad luck that

your sister's illness should get worse just now, so that we shan't have time to do our business. What's the matter with her?

ALISA: The pleurisy. She's so bad, according to what her page said just now, that I'm afraid it may be fatal. If you love me, neighbour, pray God in your prayers to restore her to health.

CELESTINA: I promise you, madam, I'll go straight to the monasteries, as soon as I leave here. Lots of the friars are friends of mine, and I'll ask them to do the same as you've just asked me. What's more I'll say four rosaries for you before I eat a bite.

ALISA: Well, Melibea, give the old lady a fair price for her thread. And you, Mother, forgive me for going away. We'll have a longer talk one of these days.

CELESTINA: Where there's no fault there's no need of apology. Besides, God will pardon you, for you've left me in good company. God grant her joy in the flower of her girlhood! For there are no pleasures like those of noble youth. Old age is nothing but a house of infirmities, believe me. It's all regrets and grudges, one continuous anguish and incurable sore, full of sorrow for the past, pain in the present, and worries for the future. It's next-door neighbour to death, an ill-thatched hovel into which the rain drips from all sides, a reed staff that bends under the least weight!

MELIBEA: Why do you speak such evil, Mother, of a state that everyone so fervently desires and hopes to enjoy?

CELESTINA: It's troubles and misfortunes they're desiring then, and plenty of them. They desire length of life because by living to be old they stay alive, and life is sweet. But as they live they decay. The boy wants to be a youth, and the youth an old man, and the old man to get older despite his infirmities. All this for the sake of living, because, as they say, keep the hen alive even if she has the pip. But, madam, no one could tell you all old age's pains, disabilities, fatigues, troubles, and infirmities, its chills, fevers, discontents, grudges, and depressions. The face wrinkles, the hair loses its bright colour, you become hard of hearing, and your sight fails; your eyes sink in your head, your cheeks fall in, you lose your teeth, you lose your strength, you walk with difficulty, and eat slowly. And, alas, madam, when on top of all this comes poverty, then the rest shrinks to nothing. Your appetite survives, but there's no food. I've never known a worse stomach-ache than hunger.

MELIBEA: I know that you're talking from experience, but the rich may tell another story.

CELESTINA: There's nine miles of bad riding on either road, madam. The rich man's glory and repose seeps away down a different channel, which is less noticeable because it is bricked over with flattery. A man is truly rich only if he is on good terms with heaven. It's safer to be despised than feared, and a poor man sleeps more soundly than one who has to watch carefully over the treasure he has laboured to gain and would grieve to lose. My friends will not flatter me, a rich man's will. I am loved for myself, a rich man for his possessions. He never hears the truth, everyone tells him lies to suit his pleasure, everyone is jealous of him. You'll very seldom find a rich man who won't admit that he'd prefer a middling estate or honest poverty. Possessions make a man restless but not rich; like a steward rather than a master. More men are owned by their possessions than own them. They've brought many to their death, they've robbed even more of pleasure and a good life. Nothing is more destructive of a good life. Haven't you heard the saying, The rich man sleeps and in his dreams finds his hands empty? A rich man has dozens of sons and grandsons who never say a prayer without asking God to take him from among them. They can't wait for the moment when they have him safely underground, consigned at small cost to his eternal resting place. For then his wealth is in their hands.

MELIBEA: You must have great regrets for the past, Mother. Would you like to have your youth back again?

CELESTINA: A traveller, exhausted by his day's ride, would be crazy, madam, if he wanted to go back to the beginning merely to arrive at the place where he is already. Misfortunes are better past than still to come, because the further you are from their beginning the nearer you are to their end. Nothing is more pleasing or welcome to a tired man than an inn. So, though youth's a pleasant time, if an old man's wise he doesn't want it back. Only a brainless fool would do that, for fools never love a thing until they have lost it.

MELIBEA: But if one wants long life one must desire old age.

CELESTINA: The lamb goes as quickly to the slaughter as the old sheep, madam. No one's so old that he can't live one year longer, or so young that he can't die today. So you haven't much advantage over us.

MELIBEA: I'm amazed at what you say. And your way of talking makes me think I've seen you before. Tell me, Mother, are you Celestina that used to live near the tanneries, down by the river?

CELESTINA: I am, please God, for so long as he spares me.

MELIBEA: You've aged very much. They're right when they say time takes its toll. I swear I wouldn't have known you but for that scar on your face. I seem to remember that you were a handsome woman. You don't look the same, you've changed very much.

LUCRECIA: Ha, ha, ha! She must have changed the devil of a lot. Beautiful, you say, with that scar – excuse my mentioning – across half her face?

MELIBEA: Are you crazy, girl? Mind what you're saying. But what are you laughing for?

LUCRECIA: Because you didn't recognize the old lady.

CELESTINA: If you can make time stand still, madam, I'll keep my face just as it was. Haven't you read the saying, The day will come when you won't recognize yourself in the glass? All the same, I went grey early and look twice my age. But as sure as you're a young beauty and I'm an old sinner, I was the youngest of my mother's four daughters. So I'm not so old as I'm taken for.

MELIBEA: Celestina, my friend, I've been delighted to have seen you and made your acquaintance. And I've enjoyed your conversation too. Take your money now and God be with you, for you can't have eaten yet.

CELESTINA: O my angelic child, my precious pearl, how nicely you speak! It gives me pleasure just to hear you. But don't you remember how the Lord himself said to the wicked tempter, Man shall not live by bread alone? For food is certainly not our only sustenance; and that's especially true of me. I often go without it for a whole day or two at a time when I'm about my neighbours' business, for one must work for good people to the very limits of one's strength. I've always put service to others before my own pleasures. So, with your permission, I'll tell you the urgent reason for my visit, which I haven't told you so far. It's a very pressing matter, and we should both be sorry if I were to go away without mentioning it.

MELIBEA: Tell me, Mother, what your needs are, and I'll most gladly satisfy them if I can, both for old acquaintance sake and to oblige a neighbour. We must always help our neighbours.

CELESTINA: My needs, madam? As I've just told you, I ask nothing for myself, only for others. I leave my needs at home. I don't bring them out with me. I eat when I can and drink when I have a drop to drink. For though I'm poor, never since I was left a widow have I been short of a penny for bread and fourpence for wine. Before that I didn't have to worry. There were always a couple of wineskins in the house, one full and the other empty. I never went to bed without a sop, and a couple of dozen sips after each bite for the good of my stomach. But now that I'm alone, they bring it to me in a little jar – God rot them! – that hardly holds a gallon. Six times a day, despite my grey hairs, I have to go out, for my sins, to fill it at the tavern. But before I die I hope to see a wineskin in the house again, or at least a big jar. Upon my soul there's no better provision. For food and wine, as they say, will take you farther on the road than a handsome face. But where there's no man in the house there's no good there either. Eve's spindle doesn't prosper without Adam's spade. But all this comes from my saying it isn't *my* needs that brought me but someone else's.

MELIBEA: Ask me for what you want, whoever it's for.

CELESTINA: Noble lady, gracious young lady, your kind words, your sweet face, and your generosity towards this poor old woman give me courage to speak. I come from one who is mortally sick, from one who believes that a single word from your noble lips – which I shall bring him concealed in my breast – will cure him. Such is his regard for your courtesy.

MELIBEA: My dear Mother, unless you explain your request more clearly I shall not understand you. On the one hand what you say alarms and offends me; on the other it arouses my pity. But I can't give you a proper answer, because I understand you so little. If one word from me is enough to save a Christian's soul, I'm a fortunate woman, for to do kindnesses is to resemble God, and the giver gains greater benefit than the receiver if the receiver is a worthy person. And one who can save a sufferer's life and does not do so is guilty of his death. So explain your request more fully without fear or embarrassment.

CELESTINA: I lost all fear, madam, when I saw your beauty.

For I can't believe God has made some faces more perfect than others and given them more charm and lovelier features except to make them storehouses of virtue, compassion, and mercy, and ministers of his gifts and mercies, as he has made yours. For since we are all human and born to die, a man cannot truly claim to be born if he lives for himself alone. He would be like the beasts of the field, though some of them indeed are virtuous, the unicorn, for example, that will kneel before a virgin, and the dog who may be fierce but will not hurt you if you crouch when he is going to bite, for he is virtuous too. So are birds. A cock never eats without calling his hens and sharing his food with them. The pelican tears open her breast to nourish her young with her flesh. Storks feed the old birds in the nest for as long as the old birds fed them when they were chicks. And since Nature has given such understanding to the beasts and birds, why should we be crueller than they? Why should we not share ourselves and our virtues with our neighbours, particularly when they are suffering from a strange malady which can only be cured by the thing that caused it?

MELIBEA: In God's name, stop beating about the bush and tell me who this sufferer is, whose malady is so strange that the disease and the cure arise from the same cause.

CELESTINA: You must have heard, madam, of a young noble gentleman of this city named Calisto.

MELIBEA: Stop, stop! That's enough, my good woman. Don't go on. So this is the sufferer for whom you've been making this long-winded request, for whom you've undertaken this perilous errand, for whom you've come to court your death? You shameless old hag! What's wrong with the wretch, that you should plead for him so passionately? He's mad. That's the trouble with him. It's true, isn't it? If I'd known nothing about his folly, how easily you might have snared me with your speeches! It's a true saying that the tongue is the most unruly member of a wicked man or woman. You evil bawd! You witch! You enemy of all virtue and plotter of secret sins, you shall burn for this! Sweet Jesus! Take this woman out of my sight, Lucrecia, or I shall faint. There's not a drop of blood left in my body. But I've deserved this and worse for listening to her talk. There's only one reason why I don't put an end to you and your errand at once. As I have some regard for my reputation, I shouldn't like to publish this wicked man's insolence abroad.

CELESTINA: If my spell fails, this will have been an unlucky visit indeed. Come here, brother devil, or all is lost.

MELIBEA: Why do you stand there muttering? Do you want to increase my fury and your own punishment? Would you destroy my virtue, to save that madman's life? Would you make me sorry, to bring him joy? Would you take profit by my perdition, make money from my sin? Would you ruin and destroy my father's house and honour to enrich yourself, you wicked old woman? Do you think I can't guess your plot and understand your damned errand? But you'll gain nothing, I can assure you, except an end to your life, which will save you from further sins. Answer me, traitor, how did you dare do this?

CELESTINA: I'm too frightened, madam, to plead my excuse. Innocence emboldens me, but the sight of your angry face keeps me silent. But what grieves and pains me most is to be unjustly accused. For the love of God, madam, let me finish what I have to say. Then you'll neither blame him nor condemn me. You'll see that I came to serve God, not to make dishonest proposals, rather to bring health to a sick man than to spoil the doctor's reputation. If I had thought, madam, that you would so easily suspect me of wicked intentions, your permission would not have been enough to embolden me to speak in a matter concerning Calisto or any other man.

MELIBEA: Heavens! Let me hear no more of that madman, that wall-climber, that night spectre, that long-legged stork, that ill-painted inn-sign, or I shall drop dead on the spot. That's the man who began to make wild speeches when he saw me the other day, and to play the gallant. Tell him, my good woman, that if he thought he'd won the battle and remained master of the field just because I listened to his ravings and didn't punish his audacity on the spot, my reason was that I preferred to treat him as a madman rather than call attention to his insolence. Advise him to give up his pretensions and come to his senses, or he may find he has never paid more dearly for a conversation in his life! Let him remember that no one's conquered unless he admits defeat, and that I retain my constancy and pride. These madmen always suppose that everyone else is as mad as they are. Take him this answer from me now. It's the only one he'll get, and he needn't expect another. Begging won't help him, for I can have no pity. And you can thank God you've escaped so lightly. I'd been warned against you and your tricks, but I didn't recognize you just now.

CELESTINA (*aside*): Troy was stronger, and I've tamed fiercer ones than this. No storm lasts for ever.

MELIBEA: What are you muttering, you wicked creature? Talk so that I can hear you. Have you any excuse to offer for your shameful audacity? Is there any reason why I should not be angry with you?

CELESTINA: So long as you are angry my excuse will only make things worse. You're very harsh. But I'm not surprised. It doesn't take much heat to make young blood boil.

MELIBEA: Not much heat? Not much, you think, since you've escaped with your life and I'm still aggrieved by your audacity. What plea could you make for this fellow that would not be harmful to me? Answer, since you say you haven't finished, and perhaps you'll atone for what you've said.

CELESTINA: A prayer to St Apollonia against the toothache, which he has been told, you know, madam, and your girdle that they say has touched all the relics in Rome and Jerusalem. The young gentleman is dying of toothache. That's what I came for, but since I was so unlucky as to make you angry, let him suffer his pain for choosing such an unfortunate messenger. I should no more have expected to find unkindness in a person of your virtue than to go to the sea and find it dry. But as you know, the pleasures of revenge are momentary while those of pity are eternal.

MELIBEA: If that was all you wanted, why didn't you say so at once? Why did you use such strange language?

CELESTINA: Because the purity of my motives, madam, made me believe that whatever language I used no one would suspect me of evil. If I didn't make the right introduction, it's because the truth doesn't need much embellishment. Pity for his pain and trust in your generosity made me forget to explain my reasons at the beginning. For as you know, madam, anxiety perturbs, and perturbation confuses and halts the tongue, which should always be controlled by reason. In God's name, don't blame me. And if the gentleman made a mistake, it's not my fault. My only fault is to have acted as messenger for the guilty party. Don't make the poorest wretch pay for the crime. Don't be like the spider that only uses his strong web on weak insects. Don't make the just pay for the sinners. Take an example from divine justice, which says only the soul that sinned must perish, and from human justice, which never condemns the father for the son's crime or the son for the father's. It's not right, madam, that Calisto's presumption should be my undoing. Besides, in all justice he's no more guilty than I am. My only profession is to serve my neighbours. That's how I live and clothe myself. I've never wished to annoy some in order to please others, though they've told you a different story, madam, behind my back. But the wind of gossip can't destroy the honest truth, madam, when all's said and done. No one's reputation stands as high as mine. I have disappointed very few in the city, and what I undertake I perform as faithfully as if I had twenty hands and feet.

MELIBEA: That doesn't surprise me, for one trader in vice, they say, is enough to corrupt a large town. I've heard so much about your wicked wiles that even when you ask me for a prayer I don't think I can believe you.

CELESTINA: So true as I pray, and may my prayer never be heard if I lie, that's the only reason I came, and I'd hold to it on the rack.

MELIBEA: Your excuse would make me laugh if I wasn't still too angry. I know that neither oath nor rack would make you tell the truth, for it's not in your character.

CELESTINA: You're the lady. I must be silent, and serve you and do what you command. You scold me today, but tomorrow you'll give me a new skirt.

MELIBEA: You'll certainly have earned it!

CELESTINA: I may not have earned it with my words, but if my intentions count I shan't have lost it.

MELIBEA: You insist so on your innocence that I'm almost ready to believe you. So I'll suspend judgement of this dubious defence of yours and not draw hasty conclusions about your errand. But you needn't be surprised that I was angry just now, for there were two things in your speech either of which was enough to make me lose my temper. Firstly, you named that gentleman who had the temerity to address me, and secondly you asked me to send him a message without explaining the reason, so that I could not help suspecting an attack on my honour. But since it was for a good cause, I forgive you. Indeed my heart is rather lightened, for it's a holy and pious act to heal the sick and suffering.

CELESTINA: And how he's suffering, madam! By God, if you knew him you wouldn't judge him as you did in your anger. I swear by God and my soul, there's no venom in him. He has a thousand charms. He's as liberal as Alexander and as brave as Hector. He's got the face of a king. He's witty and gay and never subject to melancholy. He's of noble blood, as you know, and a great jouster. To see him in armour, you'd take him for St George. In strength and courage, he's above Hercules. As for his presence, his demeanour, his character, his grace, I should need another tongue to describe them. All in all, he's like an angel from heaven. I swear to you that the gentle Narcissus who fell in love with his own reflection when he saw it in the pool wasn't as handsome as he is. And now, he's brought low, madam, by just one tooth that won't stop aching.

MELIBEA: And how long has he had it?

CELESTINA: Twenty-three years more or less, as I well know, for here I am who saw him born and delivered him.

MELIBEA: That's not what I asked you. I don't want to know his age, only how long he's had the toothache.

CELESTINA: A week, madam, though it seems more like a year, he's got so thin. His only relief is to take up his lute and sing. He sings the most mournful songs all about the departure of the soul and having courage in the face of death, just like those that great musician the Emperor Hadrian sang, I suppose, when he knew he was going to die. I don't know much about music, but he seems to make that lute speak. When he sings, the very birds stop to listen with more pleasure than when they listened to the singer of old who moved the trees and the stones, as they say, with his song. If Calisto had been born then, Orpheus would not have had so much praise. So imagine, madam, how happy a poor old woman like me would be if she was lucky enough to restore to life a young man with such gifts. Every woman who sees him praises God for creating him so. And if he happens to speak to her, she's no longer her own mistress but must do what he commands. So, hadn't I every reason, madam? Judge if my intentions weren't good, if my errand wasn't charitable, and if you have any right to be suspicious.

MELIBEA: I'm very sorry I was so impatient. He acted in ignorance and you in innocence, and you have both suffered from the violence of my angry tongue. All the same, your suspicious way of talking gave me ample excuse, and I'm not to blame. Well, to repay you for your patience, I shall grant you your request and give you my girdle here and now. But as there won't be time to write out the prayer before my mother comes back, if the girdle's not enough, come for it tomorrow, very secretly.

LUCRECIA (*aside*): Oh, my mistress is ruined! She's asked Celestina to come in secret! There's something wrong here. She means to give her more than a prayer.

MELIBEA: What did you say, Lucrecia?

LUCRECIA: I was saying we've talked enough. It's getting late.

MELIBEA: Now don't inform that gentleman of everything that's happened, Mother. I shouldn't like him to think me cruel or hasty or discourteous.

LUCRECIA (*aside*): I wasn't mistaken. This business will lead to trouble.

CELESTINA: I'm very surprised, madam, that you should doubt my secrecy. Don't be afraid, I can suffer and conceal anything. But I see that having once suspected me you put the worst construction on all that I say. Nothing strange about that. But I'm happy to be taking him your girdle. I feel his heart has already told him of your goodness to us. I'm sure I shall find him better already.

MELIBEA: I'll do more for your patient, if need be, to atone for my unkindness.

CELESTINA (*aside*): More will be needed, and you'll do more, whether you're thanked for it or not.

MELIBEA: What were you saying about thanks, Mother?

CELESTINA: I was saying, madam, that we all thank you, and that we'll all serve you and be obliged to you. For the greater the security the more certain the payment.

LUCRECIA: There's no security in this, Mother!

CELESTINA: Hush, Lucrecia my dear. Come to my house and I'll give you a rinse that'll make your hair brighter than gold. Don't tell your mistress. And I'll give you some powders too, to sweeten your breath. No one in the country makes them as well as I do, and there's nothing so unpleasant in a woman as a bad breath.

LUCRECIA: God bless your old bones, Mother. I need those powders more than the food I eat.

CELESTINA: Then why do you mutter against me, you silly fool? Keep quiet. You never know when you may need me for something much more serious. Don't make your mistress angrier than she was just now. And now let me go in peace.

MELIBEA: What were you saying to her, Mother?

CELESTINA: Oh, something between her and me.

MELIBEA: Tell me. It annoys me when people talk in front of me and leave me out.

CELESTINA: I was only asking her to remind you about the prayer, and to write it out for you. And I told her she could learn from my example how to be patient with you when you're annoyed, according to the proverb I followed, Leave an angry man alone for a while, and an enemy for ever. You were angry with me because you suspected what

I said, but you weren't my enemy. And even if your suspicions had been correct, there would have been nothing bad in it, for every day men suffer because of women and women because of men. It's the work of Nature, and Nature was ordained by God, and God never did evil. Therefore my request, take it as you will, was praiseworthy in itself since it grew from that root, and I'm free from blame. I could give you more reasons than this, only long-windedness is tedious to the listener and does the speaker no good.

MELIBEA: You behaved very wisely throughout, in keeping quiet when I was angry and in being so patient with me too.

CELESTINA: It was fear that made me patient, madam, for you had reason to be angry. And when anger's backed by power, then it can strike like lightning. That was why I let you go on till you had exhausted your whole store of cruelty.

MELIBEA: That young man should be grateful to you.

CELESTINA: He deserves more than I've done for him. I've gained him something by my pleading, but I've hurt him more by my delay. I'll go to him now with your permission.

MELIBEA: If you'd asked my permission earlier I'd have given it even more gladly. By all means, for if your message has brought me no profit, your departure can do me no harm.

Act Five

After leaving Melibea, Celestina walks through the streets muttering. On reaching her house she finds Sempronio waiting for her. Deep in conversation, they then go to Calisto's, and are seen by Parmeno, who informs his master of their approach. Calisto tells him to let them in.

CELESTINA: That was a dangerous moment! But I was wise to be so bold, and I was very patient. I should have been very near to death if I hadn't been cunning enough to lower my sails in time. How that virtuous creature threatened me! What an angry young lady! But the devil I conjured up kept his word and did all I asked. I'm indeed grateful to you, Devil! You tamed that female fury, and you provided me with my opportunity to talk to her by sending her mother out of the way. Old Celestina has reason to be happy, because well begun is half done, you know. O my fine snake-oil and my white thread, you worked everything in my favour. If you hadn't I'd break all my bonds, past, present, and future, and stop trusting in herbs, charms, and spells. Rejoice, old girl, for you'll make more out of this than out of fifteen patched maidenheads. Damn these long, cumbersome skirts! How they hamper me when I'm in a hurry to tell my news! Fortune favours the brave and foils the timid. A coward can't escape death by running away. How many would have failed where I've just succeeded! What would the new mistresses of my profession have done if they had found themselves in such a tight spot? They'd have answered Melibea back, and so lost all that I gained by keeping silent. No wonder they say, Leave the lute to the man who can play it; and that in medicine experience counts for more than learning, and that skill comes with caution and practice, as it has to this old lady, who's wise enough to lift her skirts when she's crossing a ford. And that precious girdle, I'll live to make it drag her by force since she wouldn't promise to come willingly!

SEMPRONIO: Here comes Celestina, if I'm not mistaken. She's going at a devil of a trot, and muttering all the time.

CELESTINA: What are you crossing yourself for, Sempronio? It must be because you've seen me.

SEMPRONIO: I'll tell you. Strange sights produce surprise, and surprise conceived in the eyes descends to the mind, which is compelled to reveal it by outward signs. Who ever saw you in the street before, with your head down and your eyes on the ground and taking no notice of anything? Who ever saw you muttering as you went, and hurrying as if you were going to get a prize? That's strange enough, I can tell you, to surprise anybody who knows you. But never mind. Tell me what's happened. Is it a boy or a girl? Because I've been waiting here since one o'clock, and I've been thinking your delay was a good sign.

CELESTINA: You can't always trust that silly rule, my lad. I might have been an hour longer, and have left my nose behind, or two hours longer and have lost my nose and tongue. In fact the longer I'd been, the more it might have cost me.

SEMPRONIO: For God's sake, Mother, don't go another step before you've told me.

CELESTINA: I can't stop now, Sempronio, my friend. This is not the right place. Come with me to Calisto and you shall hear marvels. It'd spoil my story to tell it too often. I want him to hear what has happened from my own lips. Because although you'll get a bit of the profit, I want all the thanks for my work.

SEMPRONIO: A little bit, Celestina? I don't like the way you talk.

CELESTINA: Be quiet, you fool! A bit or a little bit, I'll give you as much as you want. All that's mine is yours. Let's enjoy it and make good use of it. We shan't quarrel about shares. But you know we old people have greater needs than lads, especially lads like you who have all your meals provided.

SEMPRONIO: I need other things beside food.

CELESTINA: What, my boy? A dozen laces and a band for your hat, and a bow to go hunting with from house to house, bewitching lady birds in the windows. I mean little girls, silly, who can't fly away. But you understand me. There's no better pandar than a bow, for anyone can go in for a lost arrow, as they say. It provides an excuse. But oh, Sempronio, how's a person to support herself in decency when she's getting old as I am?

SEMPRONIO (*aside*): Oh you treacherous old devil, you evil old woman! You're a greedy avaricious creature. So you want to cheat me as well as my master, to make yourself rich. . . . But she won't gain much by that. I shouldn't like to be in her shoes, because if you rise in the world by foul means you sink again quicker than you rose. How difficult it is to know your fellow men! True enough, no beast or merchandise is so hard to weigh up. She's a wicked, deceitful old woman. The devil got me mixed up with her. I'd have done better to avoid this poisonous viper than to pick her up. It was my own fault. But I hope she gains something, because whether she likes it or not she's going to keep her promise to me.

CELESTINA: What were you saying, Sempronio? Who were you talking to? You're getting mixed up in my skirts. Why don't you hurry?

SEMPRONIO: What I was saying, Mother, was that I'm not surprised you change your mind, because most women are like that. You told me that you were going to drag this affair out; and now you're rushing like mad to tell Calisto all that happened. Don't you know that a thing is valued highest when it has been waited for, and that every day we kept him on the rack would have doubled our profits?

CELESTINA: The wise man changes his mind. Only fools are obstinate. When a situation changes, new plans are necessary. I never thought, Sempronio my boy, that I was going to strike such luck. A good ambassador does what the opportunity suggests. And as things are at present no time must be lost. What's more, I know by experience that your master is generous but rather capricious. He'll give more for one day of good news than for a hundred on which he's suffering and I'm trotting backwards and forwards. Unexpected and sudden pleasures cause confusion, and great confusion prevents clear thinking. So good news can bring us nothing but good, for what can we expect of a noble nature but a fine reward? Say no more, silly, and leave it to the old woman.

SEMPRONIO: But tell me what happened with the young lady. Tell me something she said, for I'm almost as anxious to hear as my master.

CELESTINA: Be quiet, you idiot. You're getting quite agitated. It looks to me as if you're more anxious to taste this dish than to smell it. Let's hurry, or your master will have been driven mad by my long delay.

SEMPRONIO: He's mad enough anyhow.

*

PARMENO: Master, master!

CALISTO: What is it, fool?

PARMENO: I can see Sempronio and Celestina coming. They're quite near, but they keep on making little stops, and when they're standing Sempronio draws lines on the ground with his sword. I can't think what they're up to.

CALISTO: You idle, careless idiot! If you've seen them coming why don't you hurry down to open the door? Almighty God, sovereign Power, what does this visit portend? What news do they bring? They've been away so long that I've been looking forward to their return more than to my salvation. O my sad ears, prepare for what's coming to you, for the comfort or sickness of my heart now rests on Celestina's lips. If only I could sleep away the time till the beginning and end of her speech! Now I know indeed that it is more painful for a criminal to wait in suspense for the harsh sentence of death than for his certain execution. How slow you are, Parmeno! You move like a corpse. Release that tiresome bar, and admit the honourable woman on whose tongue my life depends.

CELESTINA: Do you hear, Sempronio? Our master's changed his tune. This is very different from the language we heard from Parmeno and him the first time we came. Things are improving, I think. Every word he says is worth at least a new skirt to old Celestina.

SEMPRONIO: When you go in, pretend that you don't see Calisto and say something pleasant.

CELESTINA: Hush, Sempronio. Although I've risked my life for him, I would do more in his service and yours, and, I hope, receive more rewards for it.

Act Six

Celestina enters the house and is eagerly questioned by Calisto concerning her conversation with Melibea. While Celestina and Calisto are talking, Parmeno makes spiteful comments to Sempronio on their conversation. When she has told her story, Celestina hands Melibea's girdle to Calisto and takes her leave. Parmeno accompanies her home.

CALISTO: What is your news, my dear Mother?

CELESTINA: Oh, my lord Calisto, happy lover of the fair Melibea! And you've good reason to love her, I say. But what reward will you give the old lady, who's risked her life on your account today? No woman has ever been in as tight a corner as I was in. Even to think of it makes my blood run cold in my veins. I wouldn't have given as much for my life as for this old frayed cloak.

PARMENO: Lay it on thick! Mix the bitter with the sweet! This is only the beginning. You'll be going on to the skirt soon, I expect. Everything for you, and nothing that you can share with anybody else. The old woman wants some new feathers. You'll prove me right, old bawd, and my master a madman. Don't miss a word she says, Sempronio. She won't ask for money, you'll see, because that could be divided up.

SEMPRONIO: Shut up, you careless fool. Calisto will kill you if he hears.

CALISTO: Be brief, Mother, and come to the point, or take this sword and kill me.

SEMPRONIO: The poor devil's trembling as if he had the fever. He can hardly stand up, and he'd like to lend her his tongue to make her speak more quickly. I wouldn't give much for his life. We shall get a suit of mourning out of this business.

CELESTINA: Your sword, sir? What do you mean? Keep your sword to kill your enemies, or those who dislike you. But I'm bringing you life and hope from the creature you love best in the world.

CALISTO: Bringing me hope, madam?

CELESTINA: Yes, you can call it hope. The door's open for my return, and she'll welcome me better in this torn skirt than another in silk and brocade.

PARMENO: Sew up my mouth, Sempronio. It's more than I can bear. She's come round to the subject of that skirt already.

SEMPRONIO: For God's sake be quiet, or I shall send you to the devil! She's a perfect right to ask for new clothes. Heaven knows she needs them. It's only by singing that she gets her dinner.

PARMENO: And her clothes as well. That old whore wants to make up in one day and at a single stroke for all that she hasn't had in fifty years.

SEMPRONIO: Is that all that she taught you when she brought you up? Have you no more gratitude than that?

PARMENO: I can put up with her pinching and begging, so long as it isn't all for herself.

SEMPRONIO: Greed's her only fault. But let her feather her own nest, and later she'll feather ours, or she'll be sorry she ever met us.

CALISTO: Tell me, for God's sake, madam, what was she doing? How did you get in? What was she wearing? In what part of the house was she? How did she receive you at the start?

CELESTINA: She received me like a fierce bull when they've thrown darts into his hide in the bullring, or like a wild bear when the hounds are close on his heels.

CALISTO: And you call this a healthy sign? What would an unhealthy one be like then? Death itself? No, it could not be that, for death would be a relief in my present state of torment. What I suffer is worse than death.

SEMPRONIO: Has the fire gone out of him entirely? What's the matter with the man that he can't listen patiently to the news he has been longing all this time to hear?

PARMENO: And you told me to be quiet, Sempronio! If our master hears you, you'll catch it just as hot as I shall.

SEMPRONIO: Oh, may you burn in hell! I'm hurting nobody, but there's nobody you don't malign. May you die horribly of the plague! I hope it eats you limb by limb, you damned, envious troublemaker! So this is all our friendship amounts to? This is all that Celestina achieved when she made us promise to make it up? Clear out of here, and may bad luck go with you!

CALISTO: Madam, if you do not want to drive me mad and send my soul to everlasting damnation, tell me in a few words whether your glorious mission was successful. Did the cruel expression on that angelic and lethal countenance change? For what you have said is evidence of hatred rather than of love.

CELESTINA: The great virtue of the honey-bee, which the wise should imitate, is that, by working in secret, she changes everything that she touches to something better than it was. This I did with the harsh and disdainful words of Melibea. I changed all her cruelty into honey, her anger into gentleness, her hastiness into calm. What else do you think old Celestina went for, after you rewarded her so generously above her deserts? Why, to allay Melibea's fury, to suffer her bad temper, to shield you in your absence, to take the blows on my cloak, and the sneers, insults, contempt that such ladies display when first asked for their favours, only to enhance the value of them when granted.

The more they like a man the more harshly they speak. If it weren't for that, if they all said yes as soon as they were asked, or as soon as they saw a man was in love with them, there would be no difference between sheltered young ladies and public whores. However much she may kindle and burn with the living fires of love, for modesty's sake your young lady shows a cold face, a calm demeanour, a serene indifference, a firm spirit, and chaste intentions. Her words will be so bitter that her tongue is surprised at the self-control which makes her say the opposite of what she feels. And now if I tell you that her words were very kind in the end, perhaps you will be calm and patient while I tell you the full story of my visit and of the excuse I gave for making it.

CALISTO: Now that you have given me that assurance, Madam, I can bear the cruelty of her replies. Tell me as much as you wish in any way you wish, and I will listen attentively. My heart is at rest, my thoughts are calm, the blood flows freely in my veins once more, and I am happy. Let us go up to my room, and there you can tell me, if you will, the whole story of which you have given me only the hint down here.

CELESTINA: Let us go up, sir.

PARMENO: Blessed Virgin, how anxious this madman is to get away from us, and weep his eyes out with joy alone with Celestina! He'll tell her all the secrets of his incontinent and lecherous appetites. He'll ask her the same thing six times, and six times he'll hear the same answers, and no one will be there to reproach him for being long-winded. But don't you worry, my crazy friend, we'll come after you.

CALISTO: Look, lady, at the way Parmeno's talking. See how he's crossing himself with joy as Sempronio tells him how successful your labours were. He's astounded, I promise you, my lady Celestina. Look, he's crossing himself again.

Go up, go up and take a chair, madam, for I want to hear her gentle answer on my knees. Now tell me, what excuse did you give for your visit?

CELESTINA: I said I had some thread to sell. I've caught more than thirty of her quality that way, praise God for it, and some that were greater than she.

CALISTO: Greater in stature, perhaps, Mother, but not in grace or station, or wit or charm, or in descent or justifiable pride, or virtue, or beauty of speech.

PARMENO: Now the poor fellow's slipping a cog. His chimes are out of gear. The clock has stuck at noon, and never strikes less than twelve. Count the strokes, and shut your mouth. His ravings and her lies have left you gaping.

SEMPRONIO: You poisonous slanderer! Why do you refuse to listen to what makes everyone else prick up their ears? You're like the snake fleeing from the charmer's voice. Their conversation being about love, you ought to hear it with pleasure despite the lies.

CELESTINA: Listen, master Calisto, and you'll hear what my efforts and your good luck achieved. Now, just as I was beginning to offer my thread and name a price, Melibea's mother was sent for to visit a sister of hers who is ill, and since she had to go, she left Melibea behind to bargain for her, and . . .

CALISTO: Oh, how wonderful! What a rare opportunity! What a lucky chance! If only I'd been there hidden under your cloak, to hear her speak in whom God has united so many graces.

CELESTINA: Under my cloak, do you say? You'd have been peering through all the holes. For, alas, there are plenty of them, God send me a new one!

PARMENO: I'm going outside, Sempronio. I'll not say another word. You can listen to the rest. If my unfortunate master weren't mentally pacing every yard between here and Melibea's house, and imagining how she looked, and how she bargained over the thread, if his mind weren't entirely taken up with all that, he'd see that my advice was healthier than these lies of Celestina's.

CALISTO: What are you up to, boys? Here am I listening to news on which my life depends, and you two are whispering as usual, just in order to annoy me. If you love me, be quiet and you'll die of pleasure when you hear this old woman's account of the good work she has done for me. Go on, madam, what did you do when you found yourself alone with her?

CELESTINA: I was so overcome with joy, sir, that anyone who knew me would have seen it in my face.

CALISTO: I'm overcome now, so what must it have been like for you with such a picture before your eyes! Did this unexpected luck strike you dumb?

CELESTINA: On the contrary. Being alone with her gave me courage to say what I had in my mind. I opened my heart to her, I told her my errand: how you were suffering, and one friendly word from her lips would cure you of your grave disease. And as she looked at me in astonishment, astounded by this strange news and eager to hear who this person could be who suffered for lack of a word from her, or whom her tongue could cure, I cut my speech short and spoke your name. Whereupon she slapped her forehead as if she had received terrible news. Then she ordered me to shut my mouth and clear out of her sight if I didn't want her servants to cut short my ancient life. She reproached me for my effrontery, called me a witch, a pandar, a wicked old woman, a bearded malefactor, and all the other ugly names that we use to frighten children in the cradle. Then she swooned away, lost consciousness, went into convulsions, raved, and threw her limbs about, wounded by that golden arrow that had struck her at the sound of your name.

Her body writhed, her hands were clasped as if in despair, and she seemed on the point of tearing out her fingers. She rolled her eyes in all directions, and stamped her feet on the hard floor. And all the time I was shrinking in the corner, frightened and silent, but delighted by her fury. The more she raged, the more pleased I was, because I saw the moment approaching when she would yield and fall. But all the time she was frothing with rage, I did not let my thoughts wander. Far from being idle, I spent the time inventing an explanation of what I had said.

CALISTO: Tell me about it, lady Mother. For all the time you've been talking I've been racking my brains for an excuse that would have served to explain away or put another colour on what you said. But I can't see how you could have removed the terrible suspicion aroused in her by your request. When I consider your wisdom, I think of you as more than a woman. For as you foresaw her answer, so no doubt you had your answer ready. Could that Tuscan woman Adeleta have done better? Three days before she died she prophesied the death of her old husband and her two children. But her fame would have been as nothing if you had been alive in her day. Now I believe the saying that a weak woman is quicker in an emergency than the bravest man.

CELESTINA: My excuse, sir? I told her that what you were suffering from was the toothache, and that the word I wanted from her was a prayer that she knew. She's a great one for those prayers.

CALISTO: That was marvellously cunning. You haven't an equal in your profession. What a crafty woman you are! You found the remedy quickly enough! You're a fine ambassador. No one else on earth could have invented such an ingenious excuse. If Aeneas and Dido were living today, Venus certainly would not have to clothe her son Cupid in the form of Ascanius to make the Trojan queen love him. She could save herself the trouble of that trick, and go straight to it, employing you as the go-between. So long as I'm in hands like yours I'll die happy. For I shall die knowing that if my desires are not fulfilled as I wish, at least you could not possibly have done more to help me. What do you say, lads? What more could she possibly have done? Is there another woman like her in the whole world?

CELESTINA: Don't interrupt my story, sir. Let me go on. It's beginning to get dark, and you know that robbers loathe the light. I might meet with an accident on my way home.

CALISTO: What? What? But there are pages and torches here to see you home.

PARMENO: Yes, yes, to save this girl from rape. You can go with her, Sempronio. She's afraid of the crickets* that sing in the dark.

CALISTO: Did you say something, Parmeno my boy?

PARMENO: I said it would be as well, sir, if Sempronio and I were to see her home, because it's got very dark.

CALISTO: You're right. In a little while. Go on with your story and tell me what happened next. How did she reply to your request for the prayer?

CELESTINA: That she'd gladly give it to me.

CALISTO: Gladly? oh God, what a magnificent gift!

CELESTINA: Then I asked her for something else.

CALISTO: For what, my dear madam?

CELESTINA: A girdle that she always wears round her waist. I said that it would be good for your toothache since it had touched many relics.

CALISTO: What did she say to that?

CELESTINA: Give me my reward and I'll tell you.

CALISTO: Oh, in heaven's name, take the whole of this house

* *Grillos* also means chains.

and everything in it, and tell me. Or ask for whatever you want.

CELESTINA: A cloak. If you'll give the old woman a cloak, she'll hand you the very girdle the girl wears round her waist.

CALISTO: A cloak, d'you say? A cloak and a skirt and everything I possess.

CELESTINA: I need a cloak, and that'll be more than enough. Don't give me anything else, or you'll make my request look presumptuous. They say that to offer much to one who asks for little is a sort of refusal.

CALISTO: Parmeno, run and call my tailor, and tell him to cut a cloak and skirt from that Flanders cloth he put aside to be carded.

PARMENO: That's right! Everything for the old woman, since she comes loaded with lies like a honey-bee, but to hell with me! She's been working for this all day with her hints and dodges.

CALISTO: What the devil are you waiting for? Nobody gets worse service than I do. I keep a bunch of discontented star-gazers for servants, who do everything to spite me. What are you mumbling there, you envious rogue? What did you say? I didn't hear. Go where I told you and quickly, and don't annoy me. I've enough troubles to kill me as it is. I think there'll be sufficient in that piece to make you a coat as well.

PARMENO: I was only saying, sir, that it's rather dark to send for the tailor.

CALISTO: Didn't I call you a star-gazer? Well, let it wait till the morning. And you, madam, please be patient, for a gift postponed isn't lost. And now show me the blessed girdle that was worthy to encircle those limbs. My eyes and all my other senses will enjoy it, for they have all suffered together. My poor heart too will rejoice, which has never known a moment's pleasure since it knew that lady. All my senses grieved for it, all flew promptly to its aid. Each one pitied it extremely, the eyes when they saw her, the ears when they heard her, and the hands when they touched her.

CELESTINA: Do you say that you've touched her? I am very surprised.

CALISTO: In my dreams, I mean.

CELESTINA: In your dreams?

CALISTO: In my dreams I see her so often that I'm afraid I shall meet the fate of Alcibiades, who believed he saw himself wrapped in his mistress's cloak. They killed him next day in the street, and no one would pick him up or cover him till she did so with her cloak. But alive or dead, I should be happy to wear anything she has worn.

CELESTINA: You have suffered enough. For when others are resting in their beds, you're preparing new tortures to suffer on the morrow. Take courage, sir, God will never abandon any of his creatures. Give your desires a rest, and take this girdle, for I'll bring you its owner if I live.

CALISTO: A happy gift, and a fortunate girdle to have earned the honour of embracing that body which I am unworthy to serve. In your noose you have caught my passions and encircled my desires. Tell me, were you present when she whom you serve and I adore, when she for whom I labour night and day without hope or reward, gave her cruel answer?

CELESTINA: It's an old saying, that the less you endeavour the more you gain. But by my endeavours I'll get you what you're too lazy to get for yourself. Take comfort, sir, Zamora wasn't won in a day, but the besiegers didn't lose heart all the same.

CALISTO: But I'm out of luck. Cities are walled with stone, and stone can conquer stone. But my mistress has a heart of steel. No metal can harm it, no shot can dent it. Put scaling-ladders against her walls, and she has eyes that shoot arrows, a tongue that drops scorn and insults, and her stronghold is so placed that besiegers can't get within half a league of it.

CELESTINA: Hush, sir! One man's daring captured Troy. Don't despair, for one woman can capture another. You have had few dealings with my house, so you don't know what I can do.

CALISTO: I will believe whatever you say, madam, since you have brought me this jewel. O glorious girdle of that heavenly waist! I look, but cannot believe my eyes. O girdle, girdle, were you my enemy? Tell me truly. If you were I forgive you, for a good man should forgive wrongs. But I don't believe it, for had you been against me you would not have fallen so promptly into my hands, unless you came to offer your excuses. By virtue of the great power which that lady has over me, I conjure you, answer me!

CELESTINA: Stop this raving, sir. I'm sick to death of listening, and you've almost torn the girdle in two.

CALISTO: What a wretch I am! I wish to heaven that you were woven not of silk but of the flesh of my arms, so that they might daily embrace, joyfully but with proper reverence, those limbs that you encircle and for ever enclose without feeling or enjoying that glory! Oh, what secrets you must have seen of her surpassing beauty!

CELESTINA: You'll see more and feel more, if you don't babble your wits away.

CALISTO: Hush, madam, this girdle and I understand one another. Eyes, remember that it was through you my heart was pierced. You were the cause of my wound, for by providing the way you did the damage. Remember therefore that you owe me a cure. Look once more at the remedy that has come to your very door.

SEMPRONIO: You are so pleased with the girdle, sir, that it almost looks as if you don't want to enjoy Melibea.

CALISTO: What? You're mad, you're raving! Killjoy, what do you mean?

SEMPRONIO: With all this talk, you're killing yourself and everyone who hears you. Thus you'll lose either your life or your senses. And whichever way it is, you'll be left in the dark. Cut your speech short, and let Celestina talk.

CALISTO: Am I annoying you, Mother, with my long speech, or is this lad drunk?

CELESTINA: Even if he isn't, sir, you really ought to stop all this talk and all your long lamentations and treat the girdle as a girdle, because you'll have to talk very differently when you're with Melibea herself. You mustn't speak of the clothing and the woman as if they were the same thing.

CALISTO: O lady Mother, you are my comforter. Let me console myself with this herald of my glory. Tongue, why do you waste yourself on any other words but praise of that beauty whom you will probably never possess? Hands, how insolently and carelessly you touch and twist this balm of my wounds! Now the poison with which that arrow-point was steeped can no longer harm me. I am safe, for she who dealt the wound has sent the cure. And you, madam, joy of old women and delight of girls, and comforter of those who, like me, are afflicted, do not add to the torments of my shame by telling me of your fears. Leave me to the pleasures of my thoughts, and let me carry this jewel through the streets so that everyone who sees me shall know I am the happiest man in the world.

SEMPRONIO: Don't make your wound sore by pressing more desires upon it. The girdle is not the only thing on which your cure depends.

CALISTO: I know that very well. But I cannot tear myself away from worshipping this token.

CELESTINA: A token? The token was given gladly enough, but you know she gave it out of pity to cure your toothache not your lovesick heart. But if I live, she'll come to change her tune.

CALISTO: And the prayer?

CELESTINA: She didn't give it to me today.

CALISTO: Why was that?

CELESTINA: There wasn't time, but we agreed that if your pain didn't vanish, I should go back for it tomorrow.

CALISTO: Vanish? It won't vanish so long as she's cruel.

CELESTINA: Enough, sir, we've done and said enough. She's perfectly willing, as she showed, to do anything I ask and that's in her power for your toothache. Isn't that sufficient, sir, for a first visit? I'm going now. Be sure, sir, to wear a scarf round your face if you go out tomorrow, so that if she sees you she won't think I've been lying.

CALISTO: I'll wear four scarves if it'll please you. But tell me, I beg of you, did she say more? I'm dying to hear words from her sweet mouth. How did you have the courage to go in and make your request so confidently, seeing that you did not know her?

CELESTINA: Didn't know her? They were my neighbours for four years. I used to see them and talk and laugh with them by day and night. Her mother knows me better than her own hands. But Melibea has grown up since then, into a charming and well-bred young woman.

PARMENO: Come here, Sempronio, I want to whisper something in your ear.

SEMPRONIO: Go on, say it then.

PARMENO: All this attentive listening of Celestina's will only make our master go on talking. Go over to her and nudge her with your foot. That'll give her the hint to cut her visit short and go now. There's no man in the world so crazy that he'll talk to himself for long.

CALISTO Did you call Melibea charming, madam? You must have been joking. Why, she hasn't an equal in the world. Did God create a finer body? Could any painter portray such features, such a model of all beauty? If Helen were alive today, who caused the death of so many Greeks and Trojans, or the fair Polixena, they would both pay tribute to this lady for whom I suffer. If she had been present at the contest of the three goddesses, they would never have called the apple the apple of discord, because they would all have unanimously and gladly awarded it to Melibea. Consequently it would have been called the apple of concord. For every woman who has heard of her curses herself and complains to God for forgetting her when he made this lady of mine. They pine and tear their flesh with envy, and torture themselves by painful efforts to attain the same beauty that Nature gave her for nothing. They pluck out their eyebrows with tweezers and wax and creams. They search for golden herbs, roots, branches, and flowers to make rinses of the colour of her hair. They slap their faces and cover them with different coloured ointments and washes, spirits, white and red pastes – which for brevity's sake I will not bother to enumerate. So how could a sad man like me hope to serve one who was born with all these gifts?

CELESTINA: I understand you, Sempronio. Let him alone, he'll soon ride his hobby-horse to a finish.

CALISTO: Nature took every care to make her perfect. She distributed her graces among women but brought them together in her. In Melibea are displayed the most consummate of all charms, so that everyone who sees her shall know the greatness of her Creator. With a little clear water and an ivory comb she can excel any woman in beauty.

These are the weapons with which she kills and conquers. With them she captivated me, with them she has bound me and holds me in heavy chains.

CELESTINA: That's enough. Don't tire yourself out. For the file I bring you is sharp enough to cut your chain. And when I've cut it you'll be free. Now please let me go, for it's very late. And let me take the girdle with me. I shall need it.

CALISTO: Oh, poor wretch that I am, misfortune dogs my path. I should have liked to keep you or the girdle or both with me this long dark night. But since there's nothing perfect in this sorry world, come solitude and be my sole companion! Lads! Lads!

PARMENO: Sir?

CALISTO: Accompany this lady home. She takes all my joy and pleasure with her, leaving only sadness and solitude behind.

CELESTINA: God be with you, sir! I shall be back tomorrow, to bring you her answer and fetch my cloak, since there was no time to order it today. Be patient, sir, and think of other things.

CALISTO: That I will not do. It would be heresy to forget her who is my only joy in life.

Act Seven

Celestina tries to persuade Parmeno to be friendly with Sempronio. He reminds her of her promise to give him Areusa, with whom he is in love. They go to Areusa's, and Parmeno spends the night there. Celestina returns home, and knocks at the door. Elicia, who comes to open it, scolds her for being so late.

CELESTINA: Parmeno, my son, I haven't had a chance since I last talked to you of telling or showing you my love, and you don't know how well I speak of you to everybody when you're not there. I don't have to tell you again why I'm fond of you. I always thought of you as my son, or at least my adopted son, and I expected you to treat me as a son. But you repay me by contradicting me to my face, and whispering and grumbling about me in front of Calisto. I didn't know that after accepting my advice you'd then go back on your word. You still seem to have some silly ideas, and you talk for talking's sake. You neglect your profit to exercise your tongue. Now listen to me, if you haven't listened before, and remember I'm an old woman. Wisdom comes with old age, but the young are set on pleasure. I believe it's only youth that makes you behave like this, and I trust to heaven you'll treat me better in the future. It's to be hoped that you'll change your conduct as you grow older, for habits, as they say, change with the length and colour of your hair. I mean that as you grow older, my son, you learn new things every day, because youth is engrossed in the present and considers nothing else, but maturity neglects neither past, present, nor future. If you'd remembered how I loved you in the past, mine would have been the first house you would have visited when you came back to the city. But you youngsters don't care about us old folk. You follow your fancies, and never imagine that you need or will perhaps need us. You never think that you might fall ill or that the flower of your youth will fade. But remember, friend, that in emergencies like this your best resource is a tried old friend, a mother and more than a mother. She provides a good inn to rest in when you're well, a good hospital to be cured in when you're ill, a good purse when you're out of funds, a good strongbox for your money when you're prosperous, a good fire in winter with plenty of spits, good shade in summer, and a good tavern to eat and drink in. What do you say to that, you little fool? I know from what you've said today that you're in a muddle. I ask no more of you than God asks of a sinner, that you repent and change your ways. Look at Sempronio. With God's help, I made a man of him. I want you two to be like brothers. If you stand in with him, you'll stand well with your master and everybody else. He's well liked, diligent, courtly, serviceable, and good-mannered. He wants to be friends with you, and if you two joined hands it would be to your advantage. You have to be friendly, you know, if you want people to like you; for you can't catch trout, etc. Sempronio owes you nothing. So it's foolish of you not to be friendly to him, seeing that he's friendly to you. It's crazy to repay friendship with dislike.

PARMENO: Mother, I confess I've done wrong again. Forgive me the past, and advise me for the future. But I don't think it'll be possible for me to be friends with Sempronio. He's bad-tempered and I'm impatient. So how can you make us friends?

CELESTINA: But you used not to be like that.

PARMENO: True, I used to be patient, but the older I grow the more impatient I am. I have changed a lot, and, what's more, Sempronio can't possibly be of any use to me.

CELESTINA: You know your true friends when you're in a tight corner; they prove themselves in adversity. When fortune's deserted you they cheerfully pay you a visit. How can I describe to you, my son, the virtues of a true friend? Nothing's rarer or more precious. There's nothing he won't do for you. You and Sempronio are equals. You have the same habits, and the same desires, and it's your desires that will keep your friendship alive. Don't forget, my son, that you've got something coming to you, and it's being well looked after. You may know how to earn more, but your fortune's awaiting you. God bless your dear father who worked for it! But I can't give it to you till you grow up and live a more settled life.

PARMENO: What do you call a settled life, Aunt?

CELESTINA: To be independent and not live in other men's houses, which you always will do until you know how to exact payment for your services. I was sorry to see you in rags today. That's why I asked for a cloak. Not because I wanted the cloak for myself, but so that he should give you a coat while the tailor was at the house. It wasn't for my own sake, as I heard you muttering, but for yours, because you had no coat. If you wait for the usual presents from these young sparks, all that you'll get in ten years will hardly fill a hand-bag. Make the most of your youth; enjoy good days and nights, good food and drink. If you can get them don't do without them at any price. Don't envy the wealth that your master inherited, but take your share of it in this world, since you've only your lifetime to enjoy it in. O Parmeno, my son – and I've a right to call you son, since I looked after you for so long – follow my advice, which I give you only because I want you to succeed in life. It would delight me if you and Sempronio could agree, and be friends and brothers in everything. I should welcome you at my poor house to enjoy yourselves and to have a bit of fun with the girls.

PARMENO: Girls, mother?

CELESTINA: Yes, I said girls. Because I'm much too old for that sort of thing. I got one for Sempronio, though I don't love him as much as you, and I don't owe him more. I'm speaking to you straight from the heart.

PARMENO: I hope you're not making a mistake, Madam.

CELESTINA: I shouldn't mind if I were. For I'd be acting out of kindness, seeing you alone in a strange land, and for your poor father's sake too, who left you in my charge. One day when you've grown up and understand things better, you'll say, 'Old Celestina used to give good advice.'

PARMENO: I know it now although I am still a boy. When you heard me grumbling today it wasn't because I objected to what you were saying, but because I knew that I'd given my master good advice, and poor thanks I got for it. But from now on let's work together. Go ahead with your plan, and I'll keep my mouth shut. I've blundered once already by not trusting you in this business.

CELESTINA: I'm your real friend, and if you don't take my advice you'll blunder and come to grief in this business and any other.

PARMENO: I'm grateful for all the time I spent serving you when I was a boy, for it's bearing good fruit now that I'm older. I will pray God for my father's soul for leaving me such a good guardian, and for my mother's too for putting me in your hands.

CELESTINA: Don't speak of her, son, for heaven's sake, or the tears will come to my eyes. Never did I have such a friend, such a companion, and such a comforter in my trials and tribulations! She covered up my faults, and knew my secrets, for I told her everything. She was my joy and comfort, your mother was, and more than a sister and partner to me! She was so clever, and as brave and honest as a man! She'd go from cemetery to cemetery at midnight without a qualm or a tremor, just as if it were broad daylight, looking for the tools of our trade. Christians, Jews, and Moors, she visited all their graves. She marked them down by day and dug them up at night. She was as happy in the pitch dark as in the noonday sun. She said it concealed your sins. And what skill she had besides her other virtues! To show you what a mother you lost, I'll tell you something though I ought to keep quiet about it. But it's all right with you. Once she took seven teeth from a hanged man with a pair of eyebrow-tweezers in the time it took me to pull off his boots. As for entering a magic circle, she did it better and more bravely than I, though I was famous for it then, more famous than I am now, because for my sins I've lost all my skill since she died. Why, the devils themselves were afraid of her! She frightened them to death with her bloodcurdling spells. She was as much at home with them as you are with the people in your house. When she called them they fell over one another to come. She had such power over them that they daren't tell her a lie. Since I lost her I haven't heard them speak a word of truth.

PARMENO (*aside*): God damn the old woman! She's certainly out to please me with all this praise of my mother.

CELESTINA: What did you say, honest Parmeno, my son and more than son?

PARMENO: I said, How could my mother be so much better than you, since you both used the same spells?

CELESTINA: How? You'll be surprised when I tell you. You know the old saying, you can't judge an egg from the outside. We can't all be the equals of your dear old mother. Haven't you seen that some men are good at their jobs, but others are better? Well, your mother, God bless her, was the best at our trade, and she was known and loved for it by everybody: gentlemen and clerics, married men, old men, lads and boys. And what about servant-maids and young virgins? Why, they prayed God for her as they did for their own parents. She had business with everybody, and she was friends with everybody. When we walked in the street everyone she met was her godchild, for midwifery had been her principal occupation for sixteen years. Though you were too young to know her secrets then, it's only right that you should know them now that she's dead and you're a man.

PARMENO: Tell me, madam, when the police came for you while I was in your service, were you and she working together then?

CELESTINA: Are you joking? Yes, of course we were. We were working together, we were discovered together, we were arrested and tried together, and we were punished together. I think it was for the first time. But you were very small. I'm surprised that you remember, because the affair is almost entirely forgotten in the city. These things happen in the world. Every day, if you go about, you'll see people sinning and paying the penalty.

PARMENO: That's true. But the worst kind of sin is to go on sinning. Your first mistake is no more in your control than your first movements. That's why they say, A man who sins and then repents, etc.

CELESTINA (*aside*): You stung me that time, young fool. Well, if we're going to tell home-truths, wait and I'll touch you where it hurts.

PARMENO: What did you say, Mother?

CELESTINA: I was saying, my son, that not counting that time, they arrested your poor dear mother four times on her own. Once they even accused her of being a witch, because they found her one night digging up the earth at a crossroads by candlelight. They made her stand for half a day on a scaffold in the town square, with a tall painted hat on her head. But that was nothing. One has to suffer something in this sorry world if one's to make a living. And she was much too sensible to mind. That didn't stop her exercising her profession even more skilfully than before. I was reminded of this by what you said just now about persevering in sin. She was good at everything. I swear to God that as she stood on that scaffold she was so calm you'd have thought she didn't care a farthing for the whole crowd below. The fact is that people like her who amount to something, people of wisdom and worth, are the ones that go wrong soonest. Look at Virgil. He was a wise man, and yet you must have heard how he was hung from a tower in a basket with all Rome staring at him. But he was not dishonoured on that account, nor did he lose the name of Virgil.

PARMENO: What you say is quite true. But he wasn't hung up by the police.

CELESTINA: Don't talk nonsense. What do you know about church matters, or whether it's better to be hung up by the police or in some other way? That priest knew better, God rest his soul, who said when he came to comfort her that blessed were those who suffered persecution for justice's sake, for they would inherit the kingdom of heaven. It's a small thing, you know, to suffer a little in this world in order to inherit the glory of the other, especially in your mother's case. For as everyone said, she was wrongfully accused, and made to confess, by false witnesses and cruel tortures, to being what she was not. But with her courage and a heart that was inured to suffering and took troubles lightly, she shrugged the whole thing off. A thousand times I've heard her say: 'What if they did break my feet? It was all to the good, because I'm better known now than I was before.' And since your mother suffered all this on earth we must believe that God will reward her well in heaven, if what our priest told us is true. I comfort myself with that. Now be a friend to me, as she was, and try to be good, for you have an example to follow. And then what your father left you will certainly soon be yours.

PARMENO: That's enough about the dead and their legacies. Let's talk about the matters in hand. We've got something better to do than call up the past. D'you remember how not long ago you promised to get Areusa for me, when I told you at our house that I was crazy about her?

CELESTINA: Yes, I promised, and I haven't forgotten my promise. Don't imagine I've lost my memory with age. I've made two or three approaches to her in the meantime, and I think the matter's ripe. If we go along to her house now, I don't suppose she'll put up many objections. That's the least I can do for you.

PARMENO: I was despairing of ever getting her. I could never make her stay and listen long enough to say anything to her. It's a poor sign of love, they say, when a woman turns and avoids you. I was in great despair.

CELESTINA: I'm not surprised that you were in despair, since you didn't know me then or realize that you have an expert in these matters to back you. But now you'll see how much my help improves your case, and what I can do in these matters. I'm very skilful in love-affairs. Slowly now. Here's her door, see? Let's enter quietly so that the neighbours don't hear us. Wait a moment, here at the foot of the stairs. I'll go up and see what can be done about the matter we've been discussing, and maybe we'll find things are more advanced than either of us expects.

AREUSA: Who is it? Who's coming to my room at this time of night?

CELESTINA: One who wishes you well, I promise you, one who never goes a yard without thinking of your good, one who remembers you more often than herself, one who loves you dearly, although she's old.

AREUSA (*aside*): The devil take the old woman! Coming round like a ghost at this hour of the night! What's she after, I wonder? (*Aloud*) Come in, old lady. What brings you here so late? I was just undressing to go to bed.

CELESTINA: Going to bed with the hens, daughter? A fine way to make your fortune! Come on, stir yourself. Let others bewail their poverty, not you. Earn well and you'll eat well. Who wouldn't live lazily if they could?

AREUSA: Oh dear! Wait while I get dressed again. It's so cold.

CELESTINA: No, don't do that, please. Get into bed and then we can talk.

AREUSA: Yes, I shall be glad to. I've been feeling poorly all day. It was necessity not laziness that made me take off my petticoat so early so as to get under the sheets.

CELESTINA: There's no need to sit up. Lie down and get under the covers. Oh, how nice the bedclothes smell when you move! Gracious, how neat everything is! I've always liked the way you do things. It's all so clean and tidy. And you're so fresh! God bless you, what sheets and what a quilt! How white your pillows are! God save my old bones, how pretty it all looks! Now you know, my pearl, why I've come to see you so late. It's because I love you. Let me feast my eyes on you to my heart's content.

AREUSA: Stop, Mother, and don't touch me. You always tickle, and that makes me laugh. But if I laugh it'll make my pain worse.

CELESTINA: What pain, love? You're not joking with me, are you?

AREUSA: May I drop dead if I am! For the last four hours I've been racked by the womb-ache. It's risen just under my breasts and it's killing me. It's not just laziness, as you thought...

CELESTINA: Make room for me and I'll feel you. I know something about this disease, for my sins. Everyone has a womb and troubles with it.

AREUSA: The pain's higher up, in my stomach.

CELESTINA: God and Saint Michael bless you, my angel! How fresh and plump you are! And what sweet breasts! When I'd seen no more than anyone else I always thought you beautiful. But now I say there aren't three bodies, so far as I know, in the whole of the city that could be compared to yours. You don't look a day more than fifteen. He'd be a lucky man who got near enough to you to enjoy the sight that I've just seen. It's really sinful of you not to share your beauty when so many men are in love with you. God didn't give it to you to be wasted, in the freshness of your youth, under six layers of wool and linen. Don't be stingy with what cost you so little. Don't hoard your charms. They'll buy you things just as readily as money. You mustn't be a dog in the manger. Let others enjoy your beauty, since you can't enjoy it yourself. Do you think you were created for no purpose? Why, woman was made for man and man for woman! Nothing superfluous was ever created in the whole world. Everything has its reasons provided for it by nature. It's sinful to tease and torment men when you could cure them.

AREUSA: But truly, Mother, nobody wants me now. Stop laughing at me and give me a remedy for my pains.

CELESTINA: They're the commonest of pains and we all know them, for our sins. I'll tell you one thing I've seen many women do, and it was always helpful to me – though since we are all different by nature, medicines have different effects on different people. Any strong smell is good: pennyroyal, rue, wormwood, burnt partridge-feather, rosemary, musk, or incense. If you sniff it up persistently, it relieves and lessens the pain and the womb gradually slips back into place. But there's another remedy that I always found best of all, but I shouldn't care to mention it, since you're putting on such a pious face.

AREUSA: What is it, Mother, for heaven's sake? You find me in pain and won't tell me how to get well.

CELESTINA: Get along with you! You understand me all right. Don't pretend to be simple.

AREUSA: Oh, I see. Damned if I understood you at first. Well, what shall I do? You know my old lover has gone to the wars with his captain. Do you want me to be unfaithful to him?

CELESTINA: What's unfaithfulness matter? It wouldn't do him any harm.

AREUSA: Indeed it would. He gives me everything I need, and he respects me and indulges me and looks after me as if I were his wife.

CELESTINA: Even so, you'll never get rid of the sickness you're suffering from unless you have a child. He's probably to blame for it. If your pain doesn't convince you, perhaps something else will. Then you'll see what comes of keeping yourself to one man.

AREUSA: It's my bad luck, a curse my parents put on me. But this isn't the time to go into all that. Let's drop the subject since it's late. Now tell me the reason for your visit.

CELESTINA: You know what I said to you about Parmeno. He complains to me that you won't even see him. I don't know why, unless it's because you know I love him and think of him as my son. I don't treat you so unkindly, indeed I don't. I'm friendly to your neighbours. I feel happy each time I see them, because I know they've been talking to you.

AREUSA: I don't think you're being fair to me, Aunt.

CELESTINA: I don't know. I believe in deeds. You can buy words cheaply anywhere. Love can only be repaid by pure love, and deeds by deeds. Remember your cousin Elicia, whom Sempronio keeps in my house. Parmeno and he are fellow-servants of that master I've told you about, and you might make some profit out of him too. Don't refuse to do what will cost you so little. You two girls are cousins; they are comrades. See how marvellously everything fits. I've brought Parmeno with me. Perhaps you'd like him to come up?

AREUSA: A bad look-out for me if he's been listening!

CELESTINA: No, he stayed downstairs. But I should like to ask him up. Receive him and talk to him and give him a smile. That'll make him happy. Then if you fancy the idea, enjoy him and let him enjoy you. He'll gain a great deal by it and you'll lose nothing.

AREUSA: I know very well, Madam, that what you've been saying all along is intended for my good. But how can you ask me to do a thing like this when I have someone I'm accountable to, as I've told you, and he'll kill me if he hears of it? My neighbours are envious and will tell him immediately. And even if I lose him and that's the worst, it'll be more than I shall have gained by pleasing this fellow you're recommending to me.

CELESTINA: I knew what you'd be afraid of and took precautions. We came in very quietly.

AREUSA: I wasn't talking about tonight, but about other nights.

CELESTINA: What? Is that the sort of girl you are? Is that the way you behave? You'll never get a house on two floors. You're afraid of him when he's away. How would you feel if he was in the city? It's my fate always to be offering advice to fools, and they go wrong in spite of it. But I'm not surprised. The world is wide, and those with experience are few. Oh, my poor girl! If only you knew how sensible your cousin is, and what good use she has made of my education and advice. She's a past-mistress, she is! And she's none the worse for my lessons and a bit of scolding. She can always count on one man in her bed, another at the door, and a third sighing for her at home. She obliges them all, she smiles on them all, and they all imagine that she loves them dearly. Each one thinks he's the only one, her only lover, and that what he gives her is all that she needs. And you're afraid that if you take two the slats of the bed will give you away. Can you keep yourself on just a mere drop or two? You'll never have any food over. I shouldn't like to contract for your remnants. I was never content with one, I never gave all my affections to one man. Two can do better for you, and four better still. They've got more, they give more, and you've got more to choose from. The most miserable creature in the world, my girl, is the mouse that only knows one hole. If they block that up, he's got nowhere to hide from the cat. Think of the dangers that surround a man with one eye. One soul alone neither laughs nor cries. A single action doesn't make a habit. You seldom meet one friar alone in the street. You'll rarely see a partridge flying on its own. One dish that never varies soon tires the palate. One swallow doesn't make a summer. A single witness doesn't carry conviction, and a woman with only one dress soon wears it out. What can you expect, my girl, of that wretched number, one? I'll tell you more things against it than I carry years on my back. Take two, if you like, for that makes good company, as you have two ears, two feet and two hands, and two sheets on the bed; and two shirts also, so as to have a change. And if you'll take more, things will go even better, for the more Moors the more booty. Honour without profit is like a ring on your finger.* And since you can't have both together, take the profit. Come up, Parmeno, my lad!

* Engagement, but not marriage.

AREUSA: No, he shan't come up, I'm damned if he shall! I've never met him before. I should die of shame. I've always been shy of him.

CELESTINA: I'm here to cure your shame and cover it, and to talk for both of you, for he's just as shy as you are.

PARMENO: Madam, God save your gracious presence.

AREUSA: Sir, you are welcome.

CELESTINA: Come closer, you idiot. Were you going to sit over there in the corner? Don't be bashful, for the devil brought the shy man to the palace. Now listen to what I'm going to say, both of you. Parmeno, my friend, you know what I promised you, and you, my dear girl, what I asked of you. Never mind about the difficulties you put up. Few words are needed now, there isn't time for them. He has always been tortured with love for you, and, seeing his tortures now, you won't want to kill him. Indeed I can see you like him, and wouldn't mind the idea of his spending the night with you here alone in the house.

AREUSA: No, no, Mother, please! Don't speak of such a thing. Don't ask me to do that.

PARMENO (*aside*): For God's sake, Mother, don't let me leave here till we've come to some arrangement! Now that I've seen her I'm dying for love of her. Offer her all my father left you for me. Tell her I'll give her all I have. Go on, tell her, because she seems as if she won't look at me.

AREUSA: What's the gentleman whispering in your ear? Does he imagine I have to do everything you tell me?

CELESTINA: He's only saying, daughter, that he's delighted to make your acquaintance, because you're an honest girl and deserve a small present. Come over here, you bashful idiot. I want to see what you're worth before I go. Go on, have some sport with her on the bed.

AREUSA: He won't be so impolite as to come on forbidden ground without an invitation.

CELESTINA: What's this about politeness and invitations? Well, I won't wait here any longer, and I know you'll wake up in the morning with your pain gone, even if you are a bit pale. As for this fellow, he's a randy little cockerel, and I think it'll take you a good three nights to tire him out. The local doctors used to send me his kind to eat when I was young and had better teeth.

AREUSA: Oh, sir, don't treat me like this. Keep your distance, if you please. Have some respect for the old lady's decency. Don't insult her grey hairs. Go away, I'm not the sort of girl you think I am. I'm not one of those who publicly sell their bodies for cash. By my life, I shall walk out of the house if you so much as touch my clothing in my Aunt Celestina's presence!

CELESTINA: What's all this, Areusa? What's the meaning of all this coyness and squeamishness, all this fuss and nonsense? Anyone would think I didn't know what it's all about. D'you imagine I've never seen a man and woman in bed together before, or done what you're going to do and enjoyed it? I know just what happens, and all that's said and done. Alas, no one knows better than I! I was a bad girl in my time, let me tell you, just like you, and I had lovers. But I never sent an old body away, man or woman, or refused their advice in public or in private. By the death I owe to God, I'd sooner have had a smack on the face! Anyone would think from all this secrecy of yours that I was born yesterday. In order to appear modest, you make me out a squeamish fool, without discretion or experience. You slight me in my profession so as to enhance your value in yours. But there's honour among thieves, and I speak more highly of you in your absence than you think of yourself in my presence.

AREUSA: Forgive me, Mother, if I've done wrong. Come over here then, and let him do what he wants. I'd rather please you than please myself, I'd rather lose an eye than annoy you.

CELESTINA: I'm not annoyed now, I'm only speaking for the future. Good-bye to you both. I'm going. I can't stand your kissing and caressing. I've still got the taste of it on my gums. I didn't lose it when my teeth fell out.

AREUSA: Good-bye.

PARMENO: Would you like me to come with you, Mother?

CELESTINA: No, that'd be robbing Peter to pay Paul. God be with you. I'm too old to be afraid of being raped in the street.

*

ELICIA: The dog's barking. It must be that fiendish old woman.

CELESTINA: Rat, tat, tat, tat!

ELICIA: Who's that? Who's knocking?

CELESTINA: Come down and open the door, girl.

ELICIA: What hours you do keep! You seem to enjoy running about at night. Why do you do it? You've been out a long time, Mother. You never just go out and come in again. This is becoming a habit. To oblige one client, you neglect a hundred. The father of that girl who's going to be married has been looking for you, the girl you took to the prebendary on Easter Monday. Her wedding's fixed for three days hence and you've got to patch her up as you promised, so that her husband doesn't see she's not a virgin.

CELESTINA: I don't remember who you're talking about, girl.

ELICIA: You can't have forgotten, surely? You must be wool-gathering. Is your memory as bad as that? Why, you certainly told me when you took her that you'd patched her up seven times already.

CELESTINA: Don't be surprised, girl. When one has so many

things to remember, one can't keep them all in one's head. But tell me if he comes back.

ELICIA: He'll come back all right! He gave you a gold bracelet for doing the job. So d'you imagine he won't bring her to you?

CELESTINA: Oh, the girl with the bracelet, is it? Now I know who you're talking about. Why didn't you pick up the tools and get to work on her? You've seen me doing the job often enough. You ought to get a little practice yourself. If you don't learn a trade, you'll be an idle creature all your life, with no means of earning a living. Then when you're my age you'll be sorry you were so lazy now, for laziness in youth brings sorrows and hardships in your declining years. I was handier when your grandmother, God bless her, was teaching me the trade. After a year I knew more about it than she did.

ELICIA: You don't surprise me. Very often, they say, a good pupil does better than his teacher. But that's only when the pupil enjoys learning. Teaching is no good to you if you don't like the trade, and I hate it as much as you love it.

CELESTINA: So much the worse for you. D'you want to be poor when you're old? D'you think you'll always have me to look after you?

ELICIA: For goodness sake let's stop quarrelling! Time'll show. Let's enjoy ourselves now. So long as we have enough to eat, tomorrow can take care of itself. The man who makes a fortune dies as soon as the man who lives poorly, the doctor as soon as the shepherd, the pope as soon as the sacristan, the master as soon as the servant, the high-born as soon as the low-born, and you with your trade as soon as I without one. None of us will live for ever. Let us enjoy ourselves and take our pleasures, for few live to old age and none of those who do will have died of hunger. All I ask in this world is daylight and my bread and a place in heaven. And though the rich have a better chance of winning fame than the poor, nobody's content. Nobody says, I have enough. There's nobody who wouldn't exchange my pleasures for his money. But let's forget other people's troubles and go to bed. It's time. And a good sleep, with no worries, will do me more good than all the treasure in Venice.

Act Eight

Day breaks. Parmeno wakes up, says good-bye to Areusa, and returns to his master's house. He meets Sempronio at the door, and they agree to be friends. They go together to Calisto's room, and find him talking to himself. He gets up and goes to church.

PARMENO: Is it morning or what? There's so much light in the room.

AREUSA: Morning? What d'you mean? We've only just gone to bed, sir. How can it be day already? I've scarcely closed my eyes. Open the window for goodness sake, there beside your head, and you'll see that it's still dark.

PARMENO: I was quite right, lady. It's broad daylight. I can see it coming in between the doors. I'm a poor servant indeed! I've treated my master disgracefully, and I deserve to be punished. How late it is!

AREUSA: Late?

PARMENO: Yes, very late.

AREUSA: But I swear by my soul, the pain in my womb's no better. I don't know how that can be.

PARMENO: Well, what do you want, my darling?

AREUSA: We must deal with my pain.

PARMENO: If we haven't dealt with it enough, lady, you must excuse me the rest, because it's midday already. If I get back any later I shall be in trouble with my master. I'll return tomorrow, and as often as you want me. That's why God made the days follow one another, so that what isn't done on one can be finished on the next. But we can see one another again today. Do me a favour. Come to Celestina's at twelve o'clock and eat with us there.

AREUSA: I shall be delighted. Good-bye. Pull the door to as you go.

PARMENO: God be with you! . . . What joy and pleasure! Was there ever a man as lucky as I am? What luck! What fortune! To get such a gift for nothing, and no sooner asked than granted! To be sure, if I could find it in my heart to forgive the old woman's trickery, I'd go down on my knees to thank her. How can I repay her for all this? O God in heaven! Whom can I talk to about this? Whom can I share my secret with? Who will rejoice with me? The old woman was right when she said that no pleasure is complete unless it's shared. Pleasure kept to oneself is no pleasure. Who could delight in my good fortune as I do? Here's Sempronio at the door. He's up very early. I'm in for trouble with the master if he's gone out already. But he won't have done, it's not his habit. But as he's crazy at present I shouldn't be surprised if he had changed his habits.

SEMPRONIO: If I knew the land, brother Parmeno, where a man earns his wages in his sleep I'd try hard to go there. I wouldn't let anyone get in front of me, and I'd make as much as the next man. And what were you up to, you lazy scoundrel, that kept you out all night? I can only think of one reason. You must have spent the night keeping the old lady warm, or scratching her feet as you did when you were young.

PARMENO: O Sempronio, my friend and more than brother! Don't spoil my pleasure. Don't add to my remorse by being angry. Don't disturb my delight by scolding me. Don't pour muddy water into the pure stream of my tranquillity. Don't disturb my joy with your envious railing and hostile reproaches. Welcome me joyfully and I'll tell you about something wonderful that's just happened.

SEMPRONIO: Tell me, tell me! Is it something about Melibea? Have you seen her?

PARMENO: About Melibea? No, about a girl I like better, a girl who's quite her equal in grace and beauty, if I'm not mistaken. The world and all its charms aren't locked up in one woman.

SEMPRONIO: What are you raving about, you fool? I'd like to laugh but I can't. Are we all lovers now? The world's going to rack and ruin. Calisto loves Melibea, I love Elicia, and you, out of rivalry, have found someone to rob you of what little brains you were blessed with.

PARMENO: What? Well, if it's so foolish to love, I'm a fool. I'm out of my wits. But if this madness were painful there'd be someone roaring in every house.

SEMPRONIO: Yes, you're mad on your own showing. I've heard you offering Calisto empty advice, and contradicting all that Celestina says. And to prevent her and me from making something out of it, you refuse, if you please, to play your part. But now you've fallen into my hands and I can injure you. What's more, I will.

PARMENO: It's not a sign of real strength or power, Sempronio, to injure or harm others, but rather to do good and help them, and still more to want to do so. I've always thought of you as a brother. So don't let a small disagreement, as the saying goes, part true friends. You are very unkind to me, and I don't know the reason. Don't provoke me, Sempronio, with your wounding remarks. Remember a rare patience is proof against sharp insults.

SEMPRONIO: I'll say no more. Only you'd better throw in another sardine for the stable-boy now that you've got a mistress.

PARMENO: You're angry. But even if you treat me worse I can bear it. For they say no human passion lasts for ever.

SEMPRONIO: It's you who treated Calisto worse, advising him to do what you wouldn't do yourself, and telling him to stop loving Melibea. You're like the inn sign that offers shelter to others, but stays out in the cold itself. O Parmeno, you can see now how easy it is to blame others and how difficult to manage your own life! I say no more. You have the evidence before you. Well, we'll see how you behave in future, because you have a finger in this now like the rest of us. If you'd been my friend when I needed you, you'd have helped me and backed Celestina up to my advantage and not thrown in your bit of malice every time she uttered a word. When the wine's down to the dregs the drunkards leave the inn. Similarly in need and adversity a false friend deserts; he shows his true metal beneath the gilt.

PARMENO: Pleasure never comes in this life without worries to match. It's a saying I've often heard, and now I know from experience that it's true. Clear and cheerful sunshine is followed by dark clouds and rain, and pleasures give place to pain and death. Laughter and delight are succeeded by tears, wailing, and mortal grief, and ease and comfort by great sorrows and sadness. Nobody could have been happier than I was when I came in, and nobody could have had a sorrier welcome. Who could have known such glory as I did with my beloved Areusa? And who could have been brought to the depths so quickly by a few cross words from you? You haven't given me time to tell you how much I'm on your side, and how much help I'll give you in all your plans, and how sorry I am for the past, and how much scolding and good advice I've had from Celestina, all for the benefit of you and the others. She said that since this affair between Melibea and our master is in our hands we must profit by it now or never.

SEMPRONIO: I like your words well enough, and I hope your deeds are as good. But I'll wait to see them before I believe you. But tell me, for goodness sake, what was it you were saying just now? Something about Areusa? Then you know Areusa it seems, who is my Elicia's cousin.

PARMENO: Well what else could it have been that I was happy about? I had her.

SEMPRONIO: How the fool talks! I can hardly speak for laughing. What do you call having her? Did you see her at the window or what?

PARMENO: I left her wondering whether I'd made her pregnant.

SEMPRONIO: You astound me. It shows you what persistence can do. Constant dropping wears away a stone.

PARMENO: I'll tell you how persistent I had to be. I got the idea yesterday, and today she's mine.

SEMPRONIO: The old woman's had a hand in this.

PARMENO: What makes you think so?

SEMPRONIO: She told me that she's very fond of you, and would see that you had the girl. You're a lucky one. All you had to do was move in and collect the rent. They've good reason to say that God's help is worth more than early rising. You had the right godfather . . .

PARMENO: The right godmother, you mean, and that's more useful. He who shelters under a good tree, you know . . . I came late, but I gathered my crop early. O brother, I wish I could tell you how charming she is, how prettily she speaks and what a lovely body she has! But wait till we have more time.

SEMPRONIO: She's Elicia's cousin, isn't she? There's nothing you can say about her that I couldn't say about Elicia, and more. But I'll believe you. What did she cost you though? Did you pay her?

PARMENO: No I didn't. But even if I had I shouldn't have grudged it. She's worth anything. Girls are generally valued by their price; they're worth as much as they cost. You don't often get a treasure for nothing, as I did this lady. I asked her to dine with us at Celestina's, and if you'd care to we'll all go together.

SEMPRONIO: Who, brother?

PARMENO: You and she. The old woman and Elicia are there already. We shall be delighted.

SEMPRONIO: Goodness me, that is nice of you! You're a generous fellow, and you'll never go short. I see you're a grown man now, and I think God will make you a good one. So all the anger I felt about what you said in the past has turned to love. I don't doubt that you'll be as honest a partner as we could ask for. Let me embrace you. We'll be like brothers, and to hell with the devil! Bygones shall be bygones, and peace shall reign for a year. The falling out of friends always leads to the renewal of love. We'll celebrate it with a feast, and our master shall fast for all of us.

PARMENO: How is our despairing master?

SEMPRONIO: Stretched out on the floor beside the bed, just where you left him last night. He hasn't been asleep and he's not awake. When I go in he starts snoring, and when I go out he sings or starts rambling. I can't tell by that whether he's suffering or resting.

PARMENO: Tell me, has he never asked for me, or remembered me?

SEMPRONIO: He doesn't remember himself. So how could you expect him to remember you?

PARMENO: Luck's on my side with a vengeance. But just in case he does think of me I'll send his breakfast in. Tell them to get it ready.

SEMPRONIO: What do you intend to send in for our two little ladies' dinner? I hope something that'll show them you're a generous, well-bred fellow, and know your way about the world.

PARMENO: In a well-stocked household it's not hard to raise a dinner. There's enough in the larder to give us a good spread: white bread, Monviedro wine, a leg of pork, and six brace of fowls that my master's tenants brought him in the other day. If he asks for them I'll convince him he's already eaten them. And those pigeons that he ordered to be kept for today: I'll tell him they've got too high. You shall back me up. We must take care he doesn't get sick from eating them – and that our own table's well provided. Over dinner we'll discuss our business with the old woman, we'll see how we can fleece him and make something for ourselves out of his pleasures.

SEMPRONIO: Out of his pain you mean. For I'm sure he won't escape this time alive and in his senses. Well, that being the case, come on. Let's go up and see what he's doing.

CALISTO:

My peril is extreme
Death stands before my eyes,
For my desires demand
What even hope denies.

PARMENO: Listen, Sempronio, listen. Our master's improvising.

SEMPRONIO: And how, the son of a bitch! Another Antipater of Sidon, a second Ovid! Great poets they were, and the words came to their lips all ready made into verses, as they do to his. To hell with poetry. He's raving in his sleep.

CALISTO:

Heart, it is yours to grieve
And suffer pain alone
Too soon you were struck down,
Too soon destroyed by love.

PARMENO: Didn't I say he was improvising?

CALISTO: Who's talking in the hall? Boys!

PARMENO: Sir?

CALISTO: Is it very late? Is it time for bed?

PARMENO: No, later than that. It's more than time to get up.

CALISTO: What do you mean, idiot? Is the night over and gone?

PARMENIO: Yes, and a good part of the day too.

CALISTO: Tell me, Sempronio, is this madman lying? What's he mean by saying that it's morning now?

SEMPRONIO: Forget Melibea for a moment, sir, and you'll see it's bright daylight. You've been staring at her face so long that you're dazzled, like a partridge by a dark-lantern.

CALISTO: I believe you now. They're ringing for mass. Give me my clothes and I'll go to the Magdalene, and pray God to guide Celestina's steps and intercede with Melibea for me, or else put a swift end to my sad life.

SEMPRONIO: Don't drive yourself too hard, and don't try to get everything at once. It's foolish to be in such a hurry for what may turn out badly in the end. If you insist on getting a thing in a day that could easily take a year, you won't live long.

CALISTO: You mean that I'm like the Galician squire's boy?*

SEMPRONIO: God forbid I should say such a thing. You're my master. Besides I know that just as you reward me for good advice, you'd punish me for impudence. Though it's true that one's reward for good service or honest speaking is never so great as one's scolding and punishment for wrongs done or said.

CALISTO: I don't know who taught you all your philosophy, Sempronio.

SEMPRONIO: Sir, everything that doesn't look black isn't necessarily white, nor everything yellow that glistens gold. The unreasonable urgency of your desires makes you think my advice trite. Yesterday you would have liked Melibea

* Who went barefoot all the year, and then suddenly tried to kill the cobbler because his shoes were not ready.

brought to you snatched up at a word and tied in her girdle like some merchandise you'd ordered from the market. Then your only trouble would have been to pay the bill. But calm your feelings a little. You can't pack a rare spell of fortune into a little space of time. An oak can't be felled with one stroke. I entreat you to be patient, for patience is not only a fine thing in itself but the strongest resource in a stern battle.

CALISTO: You're quite right. But my suffering is too great for me to follow your advice.

SEMPRONIO: What's the good of intelligence, sir, if your will overrides your reason?

CALISTO: Oh, you're crazy! The healthy man says to the sufferer: God give you good health. I don't want advice, and I'll listen to no more of your talk. It simply kindles and fans the flames that burn me. I'll go to mass alone, and I shan't come back till you send me a message claiming your reward for the welcome arrival of Celestina. I'll eat nothing till then even if Apollo's horses have already been put out into the green fields to pasture after running their day's course.

SEMPRONIO: Stop your high-flown language, sir. Let's have no more of your poetry. Speech that's not common to all, that's not shared by all, and that all do not understand is not good speech. Say, even if the sun's set, and everyone will know what you mean. And eat some preserves to keep you going all that time.

CALISTO: Sempronio, my faithful servant, my good counsellor, my loyal henchman, be it as you say. For I know from your blameless service that you value my life as you do your own.

SEMPRONIO (*aside*): Do you agree with that, Parmeno? I'm sure you wouldn't swear to it. And when you go for the conserve, pinch a jar for our charmers, who count for more with us than he does. Just a hint... It'll go in your breeches.

CALISTO: What did you say, Sempronio?

SEMPRONIO: I asked Parmeno to go for a slice of candied melon.

PARMENO: Here it is, sir.

CALISTO: Give it to me.

SEMPRONIO: Look how the poor devil's gobbling it. He'd like to swallow it whole so as to get away quicker.

CALISTO: That saved my life. Good-bye, boys. Wait for the old woman, and bring me news when she's come. You shall have your reward.

PARMENO: The devil go with you and bring you years of disaster! May the preserved melon do you as much good as Apuleius's poison that turned him into an ass!

Act Nine

Sempronio and Parmeno go to Celestina's, talking on the way. On arriving they find Elicia and Areusa there, and sit down to eat. Over table Elicia wrangles with Sempronio. The cloth is removed and peace is made. At this point Melibea's servant Lucrecia comes to ask Celestina to visit her mistress.

SEMPRONIO: Fetch our cloaks and swords, Parmeno, if you please. It's time we went to dinner.

PARMENO: Let's hurry. They'll be complaining already, I think, that we're late. Not this way but down the other street, so that we can look in at the church and see if Celestina's finished her prayers. Then we can take her back with us.

SEMPRONIO: A fine time for her to be praying!

PARMENO: What's right to do at any time can't be called untimely.

SEMPRONIO: That's true. But you don't know Celestina. When she has business to do she forgets God and cares nothing for piety. The saints can look after themselves so long as she has a bone to gnaw in the house. When she goes to church, beads in hand, it's because food is short at home. Although she brought you up I know her idiosyncrasies better than you do. Do you know what she's counting on her beads? The number of maidenheads she's got to deal with, and how many lovers there are in the city, and how many girls she's got on her books, and how many stewards give her a ration and a bit more, and what their names are so that she shan't speak to them like a stranger when she meets them, and which canon is the youngest and most generous. When she moves her lips she's inventing lies and thinking up schemes to make money: I'll introduce the subject like this, he'll answer like that, and I'll reply so. That's how our honest old friend lives.

PARMENO: I know more than that. But I won't talk, because you got so angry with me yesterday when I warned Calisto about her.

SEMPRONIO: It's useful to us to know these things, but it'll only do us harm to talk about them. If our master knew her for what she is, he'd lose all trust in her and throw her out. But after she'd gone, there'd no doubt be another to take her place, and we couldn't expect to make anything out of her. But willy-nilly, Celestina will give us a share of what she gains.

PARMENO: You're right. Hush now, for the door's open. Celestina's at home. Knock before you go in, in case they're untidy and don't want to be seen.

SEMPRONIO: Go in, don't worry. We're all at home here. They're just laying the table.

CELESTINA: O my dear boys, my golden pearls, bless me if I'm not delighted to see you!

PARMENO: The old lady uses fine language. Of course, brother, it's all false flattery.

SEMPRONIO: Leave her alone. That's her trade. I wonder who the devil taught her all her villainy.

PARMENO: Need and poverty. Hunger. There's no better teacher in the world, no better contriver and inventor of tricks. What taught the magpies and parrots to imitate our speech? What taught them to school their tuneful throats to utter human sounds? Hunger of course.

CELESTINA: Girls, girls! Don't be so silly. Come down now, quickly. Two young men have come and they're trying to rape me.

ELICIA: They might as well have stayed away. It's not much

good asking them to come early. My cousin's been here three hours. That sluggard Sempronio's to blame for their lateness. He can't bear the sight of me now.

SEMPRONIO: Hush, my lady, my life, my love! A man who serves another is not his own master. My job is sufficient excuse. But let's not quarrel. Let's sit down and eat.

ELICIA: Of course! You're quick enough to sit down and eat. When food's on the table, his hands are washed and there's no shame in him.

SEMPRONIO: We'll quarrel afterwards. Let's eat now. Sit down, Mother Celestina, please sit down first.

CELESTINA: You must take your seats first, my sons. There's enough room for everybody, heaven be praised. I hope we shall be as comfortable in paradise when we get there. Sit down in your places, each beside his girl. And seeing that I haven't got a partner I'll put this jar and cup beside me, because I've nothing else left in life but to tipple and get talkative. Ever since I've got old my best job at table has been pouring out the wine. Because when you handle honey some of it's sure to stick to your fingers. And there's nothing better to keep you warm in bed on a winter's night. If I drink two of these little jugs before retiring, I don't feel cold till morning. I line all my clothes with it when Christmas comes. It heats my blood and saves me from falling to pieces. It keeps me cheerful when I'm about my business, and fresh and brisk as well. So long as I've plenty of wine in the house I shall never fear lean times. As for bread, a mouse-nibbled crust keeps me going for three days. But wine dispels the sadness of the heart better than gold or coral. It gives energy to the young and strength to the old. It puts colour in pale cheeks, heartens the coward, and bucks up the lazy. It comforts the brain, drives chills from the stomach, sweetens the breath of the congested, makes the impotent virile, gives tired reapers the strength to continue their labours, makes men sweat out their rheums, cures catarrhs and toothache, and travels sweetly by sea, which water will not do. It has more virtues, let me tell you, than you have hairs on your head. I don't know anybody who wouldn't rejoice to hear them. It has only one fault indeed: that it's expensive when it's good and when it's poor it harms you. So while it's good for the liver it's bad for the purse. But with all my troubles I always get the best. For I don't drink much; only half a dozen cups at a meal. You can never get me to take more, except when I'm a guest as I am today.

PARMENO: Everybody who's written on the subject says that three cups is a good and honest ration.

CELESTINA: That must be a misprint, my son. It should be thirteen, not three.

SEMPRONIO: We all enjoy our wine, Aunt. But if we do nothing except eat and chatter, we shall have no time left to discuss the love of our crazy master for the charming and beautiful Melibea.

ELICIA: Get out of the room, you tiresome ill-mannered lout! I hope your dinner disagrees with you, because you've quite spoilt mine. I swear to you I feel like bringing up every mouthful I've eaten. To hear you call her beautiful makes me sick. So she's beautiful, is she? Goodness gracious me! What shameless nonsense you talk! You call her beautiful, do you? God damn me for ever if there's anything beautiful about her, and no one would think there was whose eyes weren't stuck up with slime! Your stupidity and ignorance appal me. But no one would waste time arguing with you. Charm and beauty! So Melibea has charm and beauty? When she's beautiful, then the Ten Commandments will walk down the street in pairs! You can buy that sort of beauty in any shop for twopence. Why, I know four young ladies in the very street she lives in to whom God's given better looks than he has to Melibea! If she has any trace of good looks it's because of the fine clothes she wears. Hang them on a pole, and you'd say it was beautiful! By my life, and forgive my boasting, but I think I'm as beautiful as your Melibea!

AREUSA: But you haven't seen her as closely as I have, sister. God forgive me, but if I were to meet her on an empty stomach I shouldn't be able to eat for the whole day, out of pure nausea. She stays indoors for months on end covered in plasters made of every kind of filth. If she goes out where she can be seen, she covers her face with gall and honey, and bread poultices and dried figs and other things that I'll refrain from mentioning at table. It's only their money, not their physical charms, that earns young ladies like her praise and admiration. Virgin though she may be she's got breasts as big as if she'd borne three children; they're like a couple of great gourds. I haven't seen her belly, but to judge by the rest of her it's as loose as an old woman of fifty's. I don't know what Calisto's seen in her, that makes him prefer her to other girls whom he could have more easily, and who'd give him more pleasure. Though perhaps they wouldn't, of course, for a ruined palate often prefers sour things to sweet.

SEMPRONIO: I think each of you ladies is peddling her own wares. She has quite the opposite reputation in town.

AREUSA: Nothing is further from the truth than public opinion. If you go by what people say you'll never prosper. I speak from honest observation. What the crowd thinks is rubbish, what it says is lies. What it criticizes is good, and what it praises bad. These being its habits of judgement, please don't imagine Melibea's beauty and virtue to be what you say they are.

SEMPRONIO: Madam, the gossiping crowd doesn't forgive

the faults of its masters. So I think that if Melibea had any they'd have been revealed by those who knew her better than we do. But even allowing that what you say is true, Calisto's a gentleman, Melibea's a lady, and men and women of noble family generally seek one another out. So it isn't surprising that he should love her rather than some other woman.

AREUSA: But let's put a good face on it. Nobility depends on deeds. For, say what you will, we're all the children of Adam and Eve. Let everyone try to be good, and not base his claims to virtue on his ancestors' nobility.

CELESTINA: Children, if you love me, stop these arguments. And you, Elicia, come back to table and calm down.

ELICIA: No, it'd turn me up! I should vomit every crumb I ate. How can you expect me to sit down beside this wretch who swears to my face that his trashy Melibea is prettier than I am?

SEMPRONIO: Hush, my dear. You made the comparison yourself. All comparisons are odious. So it's your fault, not mine.

CELESTINA: Come back to table, sister. Don't give these pig-headed fools the satisfaction of making you so angry. I shall get up myself if you don't.

ELICIA: Well, if only to please you, I'll give in to this beastly fellow, and be patient with everyone.

SEMPRONIO: Ha, ha, ha!

ELICIA: What are you laughing at? I'd like to see that wretched spiteful mouth of yours eaten by sores!

CELESTINA: Don't answer her, son. We shall never be finished if you do. Let's decide on the next step in our business. Tell me, how was Calisto when you left him? How was it that you two were able to sneak away?

PARMENO: He ran off like a madman, cursing and breathing fire, and half out of his wits, to hear mass at the Magdalene and pray God to grant you strength to gnaw the bones of these fowls. He swore he wouldn't return home until you arrive with Melibea hidden in your skirt. Your cloak and skirt are assured, and so's my cloak. As for the rest, I'm not so certain. I don't know when he'll give us the money.

CELESTINA: Never mind when. Money's welcome at any time. One's always glad of anything that can be gained with no great effort, especially when it comes from a source where it won't be missed, from a man who's so rich that the scraps from his house would relieve me from poverty for ever, he's got so much to spare. Once they're struck on something, people like that don't notice what they're spending. When they're crazy with love, they don't feel it, they don't see it, they hear nothing of it. I know this from other cases in my experience, of men less madly afflicted by the fires of love than Calisto. Lovers don't eat or drink, or laugh or cry, or sleep or wake, or speak or keep silent, or toil or rest, or rejoice or complain, unless driven by the sweet and cruel wound in their hearts. And if physical necessity compels them to perform some natural act, they do it so absent-mindedly that when they eat they forget their hand as it is lifting the food to their mouths. If you talk to them they never give you a relevant answer. Their bodies are here, but their hearts and feelings are with their mistresses. Love has great power; it is strong enough to cross not only lands but seas. It has equal command over all types of men. It overcomes all difficulties. It is anxious, fearful, and cautious. It looks around it in all directions. If ever you lads have been in love you'll know that I'm speaking the truth.

SEMPRONIO: Madam, I admit that you're entirely right. For here is one who made me go about for a while like another Calisto, out of my mind, with weary body and empty head, dozing by day and staying awake all night, writing serenades, making grimaces, leaping walls, risking my life every day, fighting bulls, racing horses, tossing the bar, throwing javelins, boring friends, breaking swords, scaling ladders, wearing armour, and performing the thousand and one actions of a lover. I wrote verses, drew devices, and composed riddles. Yet it was all worth doing, since now I have won this jewel.

ELICIA: Don't you imagine you've won me. As soon as you've turned your back, let me tell you, I'll be receiving another man whom I love better than you and who cuts a far better figure. He doesn't go about looking for ways of annoying me. As for you, you don't come for a year, and then you come late and make trouble.

CELESTINA: Let her go on, lad, she's raving. The more you hear of this the surer you can be that she loves you. It's all because you've just been praising Melibea. This is the only way she can find of paying you out in your own coin. But I swear she can't wait till dinner's over for a bit of you know what. And this cousin of hers, I know what she's like too. Enjoy the freshness of your youth, while you've got the chance. If you wait for things to get still better you'll only regret it later, as I do now. I bitterly regret certain times in my girlhood when I thought I was too good for the men who wanted me. Now, for my sins, I've got too old, and no one wants me, though God knows I'm still willing! Kiss and embrace, for all the pleasure I can have now is to see you do it. While you're at table everything is allowed from the waist upwards. But when you've left I'll make no rules, since the law doesn't. I know from my girls that you lads never disappoint them. Meanwhile old Celestina will munch the crumbs from the table-cloth and gnash her toothless gums with envy. God bless you, how good it is to see you sport and play, you randy young devils! That is the way these little tiffs should end, isn't it? Mind you don't push the table over.

ELICIA: Someone's knocking at the door, Mother. That's spoilt our fun.

CELESTINA: Go and see who it is, girl. Maybe it's someone who'll join in and add to it.

ELICIA: I think from the voice that it's my cousin Lucrecia.

CELESTINA: This is fine. Open the door and let her in. She knows a thing or two about what we've been discussing though she's kept too enclosed to enjoy all the pleasures of her youth.

AREUSA: You're right there. These girls who serve ladies get no pleasures and don't know the sweet rewards of love. They never meet their relatives, or their equals with whom they can talk freely, and say, 'What did you have for dinner?' and 'Are you pregnant?' and 'How many chicks have you got?' and 'Take me to lunch at your house,' and 'Point your lover out to me,' and 'How long is it since you saw him? and 'How are you getting on with him?' and 'What are your neighbours like?' and other things like that. O Aunt, what a hard, proud, and unpleasing word is that 'madam' which they always have on their lips! That's why I've always lived my own life ever since I've been old enough. I've never cared to call myself anyone's servant and certainly not to work for one of these mistresses you find nowadays. You waste the best days of your life on them, and they pay you for ten years' service with a torn, cast-off skirt. They insult you and scold you, and keep you in such subjection that you daren't even speak in front of them. And when they see the time has come to marry you off, they kick up a fuss. They say that you've been sleeping with the stable-lad or the son of the house, or that you're having an affair with the husband or bringing men into the house, or that you've stolen a cup or lost a ring. Then they beat you and slap you and pitch you out of the gate with your skirts over your head, crying 'Out with you, you thievish whore! You shan't be the ruin of my house and its honour.' These girls expect gifts and receive insults. They expect to get husbands but leave worse off than when they came. They expect a wedding dress and jewels, but are thrown out naked and abused. That's all the reward they get, that's all their benefit and payment. The mistress promises to find them a husband, but takes even their clothes. The greatest honour you get in their households is to be sent about the streets carrying their messages from one lady to another. You never hear them call you by your right name, but always, 'Come here, you slut', 'Go there, you slut.' 'Where are you going, you lousy creature?' 'What were you doing, you deceitful girl?' 'Why did you eat that, greedy?' 'Look how you cleaned the frying pan, pig!' 'Why didn't you wash this cloak, you dirty girl?' 'Why did you forget that, you fool?' 'Who lost the dish, you sloven?' 'Why is the hand-towel missing, you thief? I suppose you gave it to that lover of yours.' 'Come here, you wicked girl, the speckled hen's nowhere to be seen. Go and find her at once, or I'll take it out of your next wages.' And in addition, continuous slipperings and pinches, and beatings and whippings. Nobody could satisfy them, and no one could put up with their treatment. They enjoy shouting at you, they glory in scolding you. The better you serve them the less they like it. That's why I've chosen to live in my own small house, Mother, as my own mistress, owing nothing to anyone, rather than in rich palaces where I should be a prisoner and a slave.

CELESTINA: Very sensible of you too. You know what you're doing. Better a crust of bread where peace is, as the wise man said, than a house full of food and rancour. But let us drop the subject, for here comes Lucrecia.

LUCRECIA: A good appetite to you, Aunt, and to all this great company of honest people.

CELESTINA: Great company, girl? Do you call this a great company? I can see that you didn't know me in my prosperous days, twenty years ago. If anyone who saw me then could see me now, his heart would surely break with sorrow. I've seen, sitting at this table, love, where your cousins are sitting now, nine girls of your age. The oldest of them wouldn't have been more than eighteen, and the youngest fourteen at least. So the world goes, and we must accept it. The wheel turns, the buckets rise and fall at the well, some full and some empty. It's fortune's law that nothing stays constant for long; change is the order of the world. I can't help weeping when I speak of the respect I enjoyed in those days. Ill luck and my sins have brought me down bit by bit. And as my days have declined, so my fortune has wasted and diminished. It's an old proverb that everything in the world either grows or shrinks. Everything has its limits, everything has its degrees. My reputation reached its zenith when I reached my prime; it stands to reason it should drop and diminish now, since I'm nearing my end. My present state tells me that I've not much time left. I know very well that I only rose to fall, bloomed to wither, and was happy so that I might afterwards know sorrow. I was born to live, lived to grow, grew to grow old, and have grown old to die. And since I've known this for so long I shall bear my misfortunes patiently, though not entirely without repining, since I'm made of flesh and can feel.

LUCRECIA: You must have had plenty of work, Mother, with all those girls to manage. They're difficult creatures to look after.

CELESTINA: Work, love? Ease and leisure rather. They all obeyed me, they all honoured me, I was respected by them all, and none of them ever crossed me. What I said was law, and I gave each one what she earned. They accepted only those I told them to accept. The lame, the one-eyed, and the one-armed passed as sound if they paid me good money. I made the profit, they did the work. And with those girls about, I didn't go short of customers. Gentlemen, old and young, priests of all ranks, from bishops to sacristans. The moment I entered a church, caps would be raised in my honour as if I were a duchess. Those who did no business with me considered themselves poor creatures. When they saw me a mile off they'd put down their missals; and one by one, two by two, they'd come over to me and inquire if there was anything I wanted, and each one would ask me about his girl. They would get so flustered when they saw me come in that they wouldn't be able to do or say anything right. Some of them called me Madam, some Aunt, some Sweetheart, and others Honourable Lady. There in church they would arrange their assignations at my house, or the girl's visits to them, they would offer me money, make me promises or gifts, and kiss the hem of my cloak – or even my cheek, to make me happier still. But now fortune has brought me down to this state in which you say: 'Bless you, I hope your shoes hold out!'

SEMPRONIO: Really it's quite shocking what you say about monks and tonsured clergy. Surely they're not all like that.

CELESTINA: No, my boy, heaven forbid I should suggest such a thing. There were many pious old ones who were not much good to me, and even some who couldn't bear me in their sight. But I think it was because they were envious of the others who did business with me. As there are plenty of priests there were some of all sorts: some very chaste, and others who made it their job to support those of my profession. There are still some of those about, I, think. They used to send their squires and servants to escort me home, and no sooner did I get there than quantities of cockerels and hens, geese, ducks, partridges, pigeons, legs of ham, wheat cakes, and sucking pigs would be delivered at my door. As soon as they received their share of the church tithes, each one would come to enter them in my book, so that I and their sweethearts could eat. As for wine, I had enough and to spare of the best that was drunk in the city. I had wine from different districts, from Monviedro, Luque, Toro, Madrigal, Sant Martin, and many other places. so many in fact that although I can remember the different tastes and bouquets, I can't remember where each one came from. It's too much to expect an old woman like me to tell the origin of a wine merely by smelling it. And there were other priests without benefices who'd bring me offerings from the altars. No sooner had the parishioner kissed their stoles than they bounded round to see me. Boys would come to my door, thick and fast, loaded with provisions. I don't know how I can bear to go on living when I think of the height from which I've fallen.

AREUSA: Goodness, Mother, don't cry and distress yourself. We've come here to enjoy ourselves. God will put things right again.

CELESTINA: I've got plenty to cry about, daughter, when I think of my good times and the life I used to lead, and the way everybody waited on me. I was always the first to taste the new fruit each season. I had it before anyone else knew it was ripe, and if it was wanted for some pregnant woman it was always to my house that they turned to look for it.

SEMPRONIO: No good can come of remembering good times, Mother, if they can't be recalled. It only makes one sad, as you can see today. For you've taken away all our pleasure. Remove the table! We'll go and amuse ourselves, and you shall deal with whatever this girl has come for.

CELESTINA: Lucrecia, my dear, let's change the subject. Tell me the reason now for your very welcome visit.

LUCRECIA: Of course. The story you've been telling us about your good times has made me forget why I've come. I could stand here for a year without a meal, listening to you and thinking of the good times those girls must have had. I can see myself enjoying that life. I must tell you the reason of my visit, madam. I've come to ask for that girdle. Also my mistress wants you to go and see her as soon as possible, because she's greatly troubled with fainting attacks and pains round the heart.

CELESTINA: Little pains like that are more imaginary than real. I should be surprised if anyone so young suffered with her heart.

LUCRECIA (*aside*): May they drag you through the streets, you traitor! So you don't know what's the matter, don't you? The old witch casts her spells and departs, and then she pretends to be surprised!

CELESTINA: What were you saying, girl?

LUCRECIA: I said, let's hurry, Mother, and give me the girdle.

CELESTINA: Come then. I'll bring it.

Act Ten

While Celestina and Lucrecia are on their way Melibea talks to herself. When they arrive Lucrecia enters first and then calls Celestina in. After considerable conversation Melibea confesses to Celestina that she is passionately in love with Calisto. When they see Melibea's mother coming they quickly separate. Alisa asks Melibea what Celestina wanted and forbids her to have any more dealings with the old woman.

MELIBEA: Oh, what a poor unfortunate girl I am! Shouldn't I have done better to satisfy Celestina yesterday when she was entreating me on behalf of that gentleman? I ought to have granted her request, for I am captivated by the mere sight of him. Then I should have contented him and cured myself. But now I shall have to reveal my passion, and perhaps he'll reject me. For he may have despaired of getting a kind answer and fallen in love with someone else. How much better it would have been to have given him my promise when I was asked rather than be forced to make a declaration myself. What will you say of me, Lucrecia, my faithful servant? What sense will you think I've got when you hear me speak aloud of what I have never cared to confess even to you? How dismayed you'll be to see me lose my shame and modesty, which I've always kept till now as a sheltered maiden should! I wonder if you suspect the cause of my distress. Perhaps you are on your way already with the one woman who can cure me. Almighty God, on whom men call in their affliction, to whom the troubled cry for assuagement and the wounded for relief, you, whom the heavens, the seas, the earth and the pit of hell obey, you who have put all things at man's command, I humbly implore you to give my wounded heart patience and strength to conceal my terrible passion! I have covered my love and desire with the shield of chastity, and given false reasons for my agonizing grief. Do not let this shield be tarnished. But how shall I manage, when the mere sight of that gentleman torments me like a poisoned sting? How frail and faint of heart is woman! Why are we not allowed to reveal our harsh and burning passions as men are? Ah, then Calisto would not be complaining, nor would I be in pain.

LUCRECIA: Wait just a moment outside the door, Aunt, while I go in and see who my mistress is talking to. Come in, come in, she's only talking to herself.

MELIBEA: Draw the screen, Lucrecia. Wise and honest old woman, you are most welcome. You didn't suppose that I should need your skill so soon? But such is my fate and fortune that I must ask you to repay me the favour you asked of me for that gentleman whom you cured by virtue of my girdle. I need repayment in the same coin.

CELESTINA: What is the trouble, madam? For the red in your cheeks is a sign that tells of some painful trouble.

MELIBEA: Snakes are gnawing at my heart, Mother, here in my breast.

CELESTINA (*aside*): Good, I'm glad of that. I'll make you pay for your bad temper, my foolish young lady.

MELIBEA: What did you say? Does the cause of my sickness show in my face?

CELESTINA: You haven't told me the nature of your sickness, madam. How can you expect me to divine the cause? I said that I'm very sorry to see your lovely face so sad.

MELIBEA: Then make me cheerful, honest woman, for I've heard great things of your wisdom.

CELESTINA: Madam, God alone is wise. Since, however, for

the benefit of mankind and the cure of sickness, men have been granted skill to find medicines, some by experiment, some by science and some by natural instinct, a small portion of this gift has fallen to this poor old lady who is now ready to serve you.

MELIBEA: How pleasant, how delightful it is to hear you! How it comforts the patient to see the doctor's cheerful face! My heart seems to be lying in pieces in your hands. With a little effort you can mend it by virtue of your tongue, in the manner of Alexander the Great, King of Macedon, who dreamt he saw in the dragon's mouth the healing root that cured his servant Ptolemy of the viper's sting. So, for the love of God, take off your cloak. Then you can diagnose my disease more carefully, and prescribe a cure.

CELESTINA: Nothing helps a cure so much as the desire to be well. So I don't think your disease is very dangerous. But if I'm to find you, with God's help, the right and efficacious remedy, there are three things you must tell me. First, in what part of your body does this pain chiefly lie? Secondly, whether you've only felt it recently, for it's simpler to cure diseases at their beginning than when they're long established and have taken root. Animals are easier to tame when they're young than when their hides have grown tough and they're less sensible to the goad. Plants grow better if they're transplanted when they're young and tender rather than when they've born fruit; and it's much easier to be quit of a new sin than one that from old habit we commit every day. Thirdly, whether your trouble arises from some painful thought that has settled in your mind. Once I know your answers, you'll see me work a cure. But you have to tell the whole truth frankly to a doctor as you do to your confessor.

MELIBEA: Celestina, my friend, you're a wise old woman and a mistress of your art, and you've eased the way for me to explain my trouble. Your questions show me that you're skilled in curing these diseases. First, my pain is of the heart. Its seat is the left breast, from which it sends pangs to every part of the body. Secondly, it has only just begun to afflict me, and I never imagined anything could drive me out of my wits as this does. It ruins my looks, takes away my appetite, disturbs my sleep, and makes me dislike all pleasures. As for your third question, I don't know how to answer it. I know of no thought that might have caused it. I've not lost a relative or any possessions, nor have I had a shock or a strange dream, and I can't think of any other reason except the fright you gave me when you made your suspicious request on behalf of that gentleman Calisto that I should send him that prayer.

CELESTINA: What, madam? Is he such a wicked man then? Has he such a bad reputation that the mere sound of his name is poisonous to you? Don't imagine that's the cause of your suffering. I suspect something else, and if you'll permit me, madam, I'll tell you what it is.

MELIBEA: Come, Celestina, what's this new condition you're making? Do you need my permission to restore me to health? What physician ever asked for that sort of safeguard before curing a patient? But speak out. You'll always have my permission so long as you say nothing that affects my honour.

CELESTINA: On the one hand, madam, you complain of your sickness and on the other you dread the cure. This fear of yours alarms me, alarm silences me, and silence prevents me from applying my remedy. You'll go on suffering therefore and my visit will be useless.

MELIBEA: The longer you postpone my cure, the more you increase my pain and suffering. Either you have no skill or your medicine's compounded of infamy and corruption and would only make your patient suffer more cruelly than before. If one of these reasons didn't prevent you, you would boldly propose some remedy, since I've begged you to do so, so long as you do not harm my honour.

CELESTINA: It's not surprising, madam, that a wounded man suffers more from the hot oil and rough stitches that sting his wound and increase his pain than he did when he first received it on healthy flesh. If you want to be cured, if you want me boldly to show you the point of my subtle needle, then bind your hands and feet with the thongs of calm, your eyes with the scarf of obedience, and your tongue with a bond of silence, stop your ears with the cotton of patience, and you'll see the old mistress at work.

MELIBEA: You're killing me with your delays. Say what you will, for God's sake, and do what you can. Your remedy can't be as painful as the cruel torment I'm suffering. Attack my honour, destroy my reputation, hurt my body, tear my flesh, and extract my tortured heart, and I swear nothing shall happen to you, and if you bring me relief you shall be handsomely rewarded.

LUCRECIA (*aside*): My mistress has gone out of her mind. She's in a bad way. The old witch has her in her power.

CELESTINA (*aside*): I always find some devil wherever I go. The lord has rid me of Parmeno and given me Lucrecia instead.

MELIBEA: What were you saying, Mother? What did the girl say to you?

CELESTINA: I didn't hear her say anything. But in any case, nothing so hinders a bold surgeon from making a successful cure as a faint-hearted friend who frightens the patient with lamentations and pitiful speeches and doleful looks. Friends like that make the patient despair of his recovery, and so hamper and worry the surgeon that his hand trembles and he can't control his needle. Your recovery depends, as you must realize, on there being no third person present. You must send the girl away. Lucrecia, my dear, forgive me.

MELIBEA: Go out, girl, and be quick about it.

LUCRECIA: Very well, madam. (*Aside*) Now, we're lost. (*Aloud*) I'm just going, madam.

CELESTINA: Your suffering emboldens me, and I can see from your suspicions that you've already swallowed some part of my physic. But I must still bring you a better medicine and more efficacious relief from the house of the young gentleman Calisto himself.

MELIBEA: Hush, Mother, for goodness sake. Don't bring anything from his house to help me. Don't so much as mention his name.

CELESTINA: Be patient, madam. Patience is the first and most important stitch. If you break it, all our labour is lost. Your wound is deep, and it needs a severe treatment. Severe pain must be met by severe measures: nothing else can be effective. Wise men say that the cure of a soft-hearted surgeon leaves the biggest scar, and that danger can only be met by danger. Be patient, therefore, for pain can seldom be cured without pain. As one nail drives out another, so suffering expels suffering. You mustn't hate or despise a virtuous person like Calisto, and don't allow your tongue to slander him. If you knew him . . .

MELIBEA: Oh my God, you're killing me. Haven't I told you not to praise that man to me, or even to mention his name?

CELESTINA: Madam, this is the second stitch, and if you haven't the patience to bear it my visit won't be of much use to you. But if you will bear it, as you promised, you'll be cured and your debt will be paid, and Calisto will be satisfied and happy. I've already told you of my remedy, and of the invisible needle, which you feel when I even mention it.

MELIBEA, I can't keep my promise. You name that gentleman so often that it tries my patience. How is he to be satisfied? What do I owe him? How am I in his debt? What has he ever done for me? What part does he play in my treatment? I'd rather you tore my flesh and cut my heart from my body than listen to you talking like this.

CELESTINA: Love didn't tear your flesh when he drove his arrow into your heart, and I won't tear your flesh to cure you.

MELIBEA: What do you call this anguish of mine that has mastered the better part of my body?

CELESTINA: Sweet love.

MELIBEA: Yes, it must be so. The mere sound of the word makes me happy.

CELESTINA: It's a secret fire, a gentle wound, a delicious poison, a sweet bitterness, a delectable grief, a welcome torment, a kind yet cruel hurt, an easy death.

MELIBEA: I'm a poor wretch, and if your diagnosis is true I'm not likely to recover. For to judge by your way of describing it my disease has so many opposite qualities that what will assuage it in one way will inflame and aggravate it in the other.

CELESTINA: Don't despair of a cure, my dear noble young lady. When the great God sends a wound he follows it with a remedy. What's more, I know where the herb grows that will bring you relief.

MELIBEA: What's it called?

CELESTINA: I dare not tell you.

MELIBEA: Speak up. Don't be afraid.

CELESTINA: Calisto. . . Oh, for goodness sake, lady Melibea, what weakness is this? She has fainted? That's unlucky. Lift up your head. Is this what my errand brings me to? If she dies they'll kill me, and even if she lives they'll find me out. For she won't be strong enough to keep quiet about her sickness and my cure. My dear lady Melibea, my angel, what's the matter? What's happened to your sweet tongue? Where's your lovely colour? Open those bright eyes. Lucrecia, Lucrecia, come here at once! Your mistress has fainted in my arms. Run down and fetch a jug of water.

MELIBEA: Gently, gently, and I'll try to get up. Don't alarm the house.

CELESTINA: Oh dear dear! Don't faint again, lady. Talk to me as you did before.

MELIBEA: I will, and better than before. Hush now, don't exhaust me.

CELESTINA: What do you want me to do, my precious? What was it that came over you? I think my stitches are breaking.

MELIBEA: It's my honour and modesty that are breaking. My sense of shame is getting weak. They were so natural to me, so much a part of my being that they couldn't so lightly leave my face without, for a while at least, taking the colour from my cheeks, and my speech and most of my senses as well. So now, my good doctor, my faithful secretary, it's no good my trying to conceal from you what you so obviously know. Many days have passed since that noble gentleman declared his love to me. His speech distressed me, but now that you have spoken of him again it fills me with joy. Your stitches have closed my wound, and I have come to love you. When you took him my girdle you made me his prisoner. His toothache was a torment to me, his suffering an agony. I commend you most highly for your great patience, your wise boldness, your generous endeavours, your careful and faithful scheming, your soothing words, your wisdom, your extreme solicitude, and your fortunate persistence. The gentleman is greatly in your debt, and I even more so. For no matter how much I reproached you, nothing daunted your courage or your unfailing confidence in your skill. Like a faithful servant, you have been most diligent when most abused, most industrious when in least favour, and most cheerful when I spoke most harshly. The angrier I became the more humble you were. Laying aside all fear, you have wormed from my heart the secret that I never thought I should have confessed to you or anyone else.

CELESTINA: My dear lady and friend, do not be surprised. Confidence in my purpose gives me courage to bear the scruples and scoldings of sheltered maidens like yourself. When I was on the way here, it's true, and even when I was already in the house I had not made up my mind, and was still very doubtful whether I could reveal my errand. Your father's power alarmed me, but when I thought how good and kind you are I took strength. I was half frightened and half confident. But now that you have revealed this great matter to me, say what you wish, confide your secrets to my bosom, and leave the solution of this problem in my hands. I will see to it that your desires and Calisto's are soon fulfilled.

MELIBEA: O Calisto, my dear lord, my sweet and gentle joy! If your heart feels as mine does now, I am surprised that absence gives you leave to live! Mother, mistress, if you value my life, contrive to let me see him soon.

CELESTINA: You shall see him and speak to him.

MELIBEA: Speak to him? That's impossible.

CELESTINA: Nothing is impossible if you really want it.

MELIBEA: Tell me how.

CELESTINA: I've thought, and I'll tell you. At your door.

MELIBEA: When?

CELESTINA: Tonight.

MELIBEA: If you can manage that I'll worship you. Tell me, at what time?

CELESTINA: At midnight.

MELIBEA: Go then, madam, my loyal friend. Speak to that gentleman, and tell him to come very quietly. Arrange for him to be here at midnight, if he will, just as you said.

CELESTINA: Here comes your mother. Good-bye.

MELIBEA: Lucrecia, my friend, my loyal servant and faithful confidante, you see that it was beyond my power. My love for Calisto has made me his prisoner. I beg of you, in God's name, to keep my secret, so that I may enjoy my gentle love, and I will hold you as dear as your true service deserves.

LUCRECIA: Madam, I knew your trouble long ago, and I have kept it secret. It has grieved me to see you in such distress. The more you tried to hide from me the fire that burnt you, the more its flames revealed themselves in the colour of your cheeks, the restlessness of your heart, the trembling of your limbs, your lack of appetite and broken sleep. Against your will, you gave repeated signs of your pain. But when the mistress is overcome by desire or wild passion, the servant can only be diligent in her duties. She must not offer specious advice. So I suffered, was silent though afraid, and faithfully dissembled, though I believe that good advice might have been more useful than soft flattery. But since your choice now, madam, is between death and love, it's better to choose the lesser evil.

ALISA: Why do you come here every day, neighbour?

CELESTINA: The thread I delivered yesterday was a little underweight, and I came to make good the difference, as I promised. I have brought the rest and now I'm going. Good-bye to you.

ALISA: And to you. What did the old woman want, Melibea?

MELIBEA: To sell me a little whitening.

ALISA: That's more likely than the tale she told me. The old wretch was afraid I should object to her visit, and so she lied. Beware of her, daughter. She's a cunning cheat, one of these thieves who always hang round rich men's houses. With her tricks and false trading, she can corrupt virtue itself and destroy reputations. If she visits a house often it arouses suspicion.

LUCRECIA (*aside*): The mistress is wise too late.

ALISA: I entreat you, daughter, don't welcome her if she comes again when I'm not here. Give her a sharp reception. She'll judge of your virtue by that, and stay away in future. For true virtue's more frightening than a sword.

MELIBEA: Is that the sort of woman she is? Never again then! I'm very glad you warned me. Now I know her I'll be on my guard.

Act Eleven

After leaving Melibea, Celestina goes through the streets talking to herself. She sees Sempronio and Parmeno on the way to the Magdalene to fetch their master. When Celestina arrives, Sempronio is speaking to Calisto and they go to Calisto's house. Here Celestina tells him her message, and the arrangement she has made with Melibea. During their talk, Parmeno and Sempronio are also holding a conversation. Celestina takes leave of Calisto, goes home and knocks at the door, which Elicia opens. They sup and go to bed.

CELESTINA: O lord, I'm so overburdened with joy that I can hardly stagger home. There are Parmeno and Sempronio going into the Magdalene. I'll follow them, and if Calisto happens to be there we'll go to his house and claim our reward for bringing him good news.

SEMPRONIO: Sir, you've been here so long that everyone's noticed you. Don't get yourself talked about, for goodness sake, for those who are too devout are always called hypocrites. They'll say you can't leave the saints in peace. If you're sick, keep your sickness at home where it's out of sight, and don't reveal your troubles to strangers. After all, the game's in the hands of an expert now.

CALISTO: In whose?

SEMPRONIO: In Celestina's.

CELESTINA: What's this about Celestina? What are you saying about this slave of Calisto's? I've chased you right down the Calle del Arcediano, but in these long skirts I couldn't catch you up.

CALISTO: O jewel of the world, easer of my pain, mirror of my eyes! My heart leaps at the sight of your honest face, your aged virtue! Tell me why you've come. What news do you bring? You look so happy. What does my life depend on?

CELESTINA: My tongue.

CALISTO: My glory and comfort, what is it you say? Explain yourself more clearly.

CELESTINA: Let's leave the church, sir, and on our way to your house I'll tell you something that will make you truly happy.

PARMENO: The old woman's in high spirits, brother. She must have good news.

SEMPRONIO: Listen.

CELESTINA: I've been working all day on your affairs, sir, to the neglect of others more profitable. I've disappointed several people to please you, and it's cost me more than you might imagine. But it's been time well spent, since I bring you such good news. Now listen and I'll tell you briefly, since I'm not one for many words. I've just left Melibea, and she's yours.

CALISTO: What do I hear?

CELESTINA: She's no longer her own mistress, she's yours. She will obey you rather than her father Pleberio.

CALISTO: Mind what you're saying, Mother. If you talk like that these boys will say you're mad. Melibea is my lady, Melibea is my goddess, Melibea is my life. I am her prisoner. I am her slave.

SEMPRONIO: You have too little self-confidence, sir. You undervalue yourself. That's what makes you speak like this and interrupt her report. You worry us all with this foolish talk. Why are you crossing yourself? Give her something for her labours. It's only right that you should. To judge by what she's said, she's certainly earned it.

CALISTO: Yes, of course. Mother, I know very well that my trifling gift can never reward your labours. Instead of the cloak and skirt, part of the profit of which would go to the tailor, take this little chain, hang it round your neck, and continue to bring me joy with your story.

PARMENO (*to Sempronio*): A little chain he calls it! D'you hear that, Sempronio? He doesn't count the cost. I promise you I wouldn't give away my share in it for half a gold mark, however unfairly the old woman divides it.

SEMPRONIO: Quiet, or the master will hear you. If he does we shall have to calm him down and deal with you too, for I assure you he's fed up with all your complaints. If you love me, brother, listen and be quiet. That's what God gave you two ears and only one mouth for.

PARMENO: Listen to the devil! He's hanging on the old woman's lips, deaf and dumb and blind. He's so bemused that if we were to thumb our noses at him he would think we were praying to God for the success of his affair.

SEMPRONIO: Shut up and listen carefully to Celestina. I swear to God she deserves all he'll give her and more. She's got a tale to tell him.

CELESTINA: My lord Calisto, you've been very generous to this weak old woman. But since a gift or favour should be judged great or small according to the person who gives it, I will not make too much of my lack of merit, though both in quantity and quality this gift exceeds my deserts. I will measure it rather by your generosity, compared with which it is as nothing. I've earned it by giving you back your health which you had lost, your heart which was missing, and your wits which were disturbed. Melibea yearns for you more than you yearn for Melibea. She loves you and longs to see you. She spends more hours thinking of you than of herself. She calls herself yours and considers that a title to freedom. With it she calms the flames that burn her more than they burn you.

CALISTO: Am I really here, boys? Did I really hear those

words? Look and make sure that I'm awake. Is it day or night? Lord God, heavenly Father, don't let this prove a dream, I beg of you. But I'm awake! If you're mocking me, madam, and making this story up to please me, don't be afraid to say so. For you've earned more than I paid you by your endeavours alone.

CELESTINA: A heart suffering from desire can never believe good news or doubt bad. But you'll see whether I'm mocking you or not if you go to her house tonight as the clock strikes twelve, and talk with her at her door, as I have arranged with her you shall. You'll hear from her own lips better than I can tell you, what efforts I made, how much she desires you and loves you, and who brought this about.

CALISTO: Well, could I ever have hoped for such a thing? Could I ever have expected anything like this to happen to me? I shall die on the way there. I can't contain so much happiness. I don't deserve such a reward. I am not worthy to speak to a lady such as she, and at her own wish and request.

CELESTINA: It is more difficult to bear good fortune than bad, as I've always heard. For good fortune doesn't bring peace, and troubles have their consolations. Why not consider your own worth, lord Calisto? Why not consider the time you have spent in her service? Why not consider who it is that you've got as an intermediary? Also that till now you've always been doubtful of your success, and yet you've persisted. Surely you don't want to end your life now that I tell you your suffering is over? Think, think that Celestina is helping you, and that even if you lacked all the qualities of a lover she'd pass you off for the most accomplished gallant in the world. She'd level the sharpest rocks to make you a road, and calm the most raging torrents to let you cross dry-shod. You don't know who you've taken into your service.

CALISTO: Just a moment, madam. What was it you said? That she's longing to come?

CELESTINA: Yes, she'd come on her knees.

SEMPRONIO: I hope this isn't a bit of witchcraft that'll get us all in her power. Be careful, Mother. That's how they conceal rat-poison. They put it in bread, so that the rats shan't taste it.

PARMENO: I never heard you say a truer word. The lady's sudden yielding and her speedy love for Celestina arouse my suspicions. Perhaps she's tricking us with her sweet and ready talk, only to rob us when we're off our guard, as gipsies do when they read our destiny in our hands. For truly, Mother, treachery is often masked by soft words. The cunning decoy lures the partridge into his net by gentle rustling. The sweet siren's song deceives the unwary sailor. And similarly, perhaps, by her sudden mildness and yielding Melibea is trying to capture the lot of us without danger to herself, and thus vindicate her innocence at the cost of Calisto's honour and our lives. So like a new born lamb that does not care whether it sucks its own dam or another, with no danger to herself she will avenge Calisto's insolence on us all. For with all her servants she could take master and men at one sweep while you were scratching yourself in front of the fire and thinking: 'The bell-ringer's safe ...'

CALISTO: Shut up, you foolish, suspicious rascals! Are you trying to make me believe that angels can do evil? For Melibea's an angel in disguise come down to sojourn amongst us.

SEMPRONIO (*to Parmeno*): Back to those heresies again? Listen to him, Parmeno! But don't let it worry you. If there's treachery he can pay for us all. We can show a clean pair of heels.

CELESTINA: You're quite right, sir. You fellows are full of

idle suspicions. I've done everything I undertook to do. I've brought you happiness, lord Calisto. May God bless you and preserve you. I'm contented now, and I shall go. If you need me further for this or any other business, I'm completely at your service.

PARMENO: Ha, ha, ha!

SEMPRONIO: What on earth are you laughing at?

PARMENO: At the old woman's haste to get away. She can't wait to get that chain out of the house. She can't believe it's hers or that he really gave it to her, because she no more deserves it than Calisto deserves Melibea.

SEMPRONIO: What else would you expect her to do? She knows and understands what we think and don't say. The old bawd's usual price for mending maidenheads is seven for twopence, and suddenly she's given a load of gold. So the first thing she does is to depart with it quickly; because she's afraid it'll be taken away again now that she's done her part in the business. But she'd better take care she divides it up, or we'll tear her soul from her body!

CALISTO: God be with you, Mother. I want to rest and take a bit of sleep to make up for last night and prepare myself for this one.

*

Celestina knocks at her door.

ELICIA: Who's that?

CELESTINA: It's me, girl. Let me in.

ELICIA: What makes you so late? You shouldn't stay out like this. You're too old. You'll stumble and fall one day, and it'll be the death of you.

CELESTINA: I'm not afraid of that. I always pick my path by daylight if I'm going out at night. And I never go on the footway or pavement but keep in the middle of the road, because, as the proverb says, It's never safe to walk under the wall, but stick to the level and you won't stumble. I'd rather dirty my boots in the mud than get a bloody head from bumping it on some stone. But that isn't what's worrying you.

ELICIA: Well, what is worrying me then?

CELESTINA: That your guest walked out and left you alone.

ELICIA: Oh, that was four hours ago. Why should I remember that?

CELESTINA: The quicker they leave the less you like it, and that's only reasonable. But let's forget that he left early and I've come late. Let's have our supper and go to bed.

Act Twelve

At midnight Calisto, Sempronio, and Parmeno go to Melibea's house, all armed. Lucrecia and Melibea are at the door, waiting for Calisto. Lucrecia speaks to him first, and then calls Melibea. After her departure Melibea and Calisto speak through the door. Meanwhile Sempronio and Parmeno also speak together. Hearing people in the street, they prepare to run away. Calisto says good-bye to Melibea after arranging to come back on the following night. Pleberio is awoken by the noise in the street, and rouses his wife Alisa. They ask Melibea who is moving in her room. Melibea answers that she woke up thirsty. Calisto talks to his servants as they walk home, and then goes to bed. Parmeno and Sempronio go to Celestina's to demand their share of the booty. She puts them off. A quarrel breaks out, and they attack her and kill her. Elicia screams and the watch comes to arrest them both.

CALISTO: What did the clock strike then, lads?

SEMPRONIO: Ten o'clock.

CALISTO: Oh, how I loathe carelessness in servants! And what an example of it you've given me by your carelessness tonight when I am vigilant! Why do you give the first answer that comes into your head, you brainless idiot, when you know how much it matters to me whether it's ten or eleven? A poor look-out for me if I had gone to sleep relying on Sempronio for an answer, and he, having called eleven o'clock ten, had called twelve o'clock eleven! Melibea would have come to the door, found that I was not there, and gone away. Then my pain would not have been cured, and my desires would remain unsatisfied. That saying is certainly true, that other men's troubles are easy to bear.

SEMPRONIO: It seems just as wrong to me to ask when you know the answer as to reply when you don't. I think we should spend this next hour better, sir, in putting on our armour than in picking quarrels.

CALISTO (*aside*): The fool's talking sense. This is not a time for getting angry. Better think about what has happened than about what might, not about the harm that might have come through his neglect but about the advantage that will come through my vigilance. I must master my anger, and either dismiss it or assuage it. Take down my cuirass, Parmeno, and put on your own, my lads. Then we shall be well prepared. For, as they say, well armed is half the battle.

PARMENO: Here it is, sir.

CALISTO: Help me put it on. Look outside, Sempronio, and see if there's anyone in the street.

SEMPRONIO: There's no sign of anyone, and even if there were it's far too dark for us to be seen or recognized.

CALISTO: Let's go by this street. Though it takes us out of our way we're less likely to meet anyone. Now it's striking twelve. Midnight is a good time.

PARMENO: We're nearly there.

CALISTO: We're very punctual. Go to the house, Parmeno, and see if the lady is at the door.

PARMENO: I, sir? God forbid I should spoil what I didn't take. You'd better show yourself first, sir. She'd be upset if she saw me, for she'd think that many knew what she would like to keep secret. She would certainly take fright and might think that you'd betrayed her.

CALISTO: You're right indeed, Parmeno. Your sound advice has saved me. If I'd driven her away by my foolishness, you'd have carried me home a corpse. I'll go to the door. Stay here, both of you.

PARMENO: What do you think of that, Sempronio? Our fool

of a master wanted to use me as a shield to protect him from the first danger. How am I to know who is hiding behind those closed doors? How am I to know there's no treachery in this? How am I to know that Melibea isn't waiting to pay our master out for his insolence? What's more, we're not sure the old woman was telling the truth. This is no laughing matter, Parmeno. You might be struck dead and never know who did it. Play the flatterer to please your master and you'll weep for other men's troubles. If you don't take Celestina's advice you'll certainly come to grief. Offer faithful counsel and warnings, and they'll earn you a beating. Go on the way you're doing, and you'll end in the street. Well, having escaped that danger I feel as if I were beginning a new life.

SEMPRONIO: Quietly, quietly, Parmeno! Don't make all that noise just because you're in high spirits, or someone may hear you.

PARMENO: Nonsense, brother, I'm not in high spirits. When I refused him just now I managed to convince him that it was for his good, but it was really for my own safety. Nobody knows how to look after his skin better than I do! Watch me carefully and you'll see me do a thing or two that not everyone will understand, not Calisto indeed, nor anyone else who pokes his nose into this business. I'm certain that this young lady is serving as a bait or as buzzard-meat, and anyone who's caught by that sort of food pays dearly for his meal.

SEMPRONIO: Don't worry about your suspicions, even if they prove correct. Be ready to run like old Nick the moment you hear a shout.

PARMENO: You and I were brought up in the same school. We're in agreement. I'm wearing light breeches and leggings so that I can run away quickly. I'm grateful to you, brother, for confessing to me what I should have been too shy to confess to you. If our master's discovered, he won't escape from Pleberio's servants, I'm afraid, to inquire what we were doing or accuse us of running away.

SEMPRONIO: Agreement among fellow servants is a very good and useful thing, friend Parmeno. If Celestina did nothing else for us at least she brought us together.

PARMENO: That's obvious and undeniable. If we were shy of one another and of the word coward, we'd await our deaths here beside our master, little though he deserves it.

SEMPRONIO: Melibea must have come down. Listen, and you'll hear them whispering.

PARMENO: I'm afraid it may not be she but someone imitating her voice.

SEMPRONIO: God save us from traitors! I hope they haven't blocked the street to cut off our escape. That's the only thing I'm frightened of.

CALISTO (*aside*): To judge by the noise there's more than one person there. But, whoever it is, I'll speak. St, st! My lady!

LUCRECIA: That's Calisto's voice, I'll go. Who's speaking? Who's that outside?

CALISTO: One who comes in answer to your command.

LUCRECIA: Why don't you come over here, madam? You needn't be afraid. It is that gentleman.

MELIBEA: Speak quietly, you fool! Make sure that it's he.

LUCRECIA: Come over, madam, it certainly is. I recognize him by his voice.

CALISTO: I'm sure this is a trick. It isn't Melibea's voice. What's that noise? I'm lost. But, dead or alive, I'll not leave this spot.

MELIBEA: Go and rest a little, Lucrecia. St! Sir! What's your name? And who told you to come here?

CALISTO: One who has the right to command the whole world, one whom I am not worthy to serve. Do not be afraid, madam, to show yourself to this captive of your beauty. The sweet sound of your voice, which has never left my ears, assures me that you are my lady Melibea. I am your servant Calisto.

MELIBEA: The great audacity of your messages has compelled me to meet and speak to you, my lord Calisto. You had my reply to your first one, and I don't know what more you expect of my kindness than I gave you then. Renounce your vain and foolish suit, or my honour and person will fall under suspicion. Go and leave me in peace. This is what I've come to ask of you. Do not put my reputation at the mercy of slanderers.

CALISTO: When a heart is stoutly fortified against adversity, no misfortune is strong enough to breach its walls. But alas for me, unarmed and unprovided against deceit and treachery, I came to you tonight, confident of your love. So anything that calls it into question tortures and wounds me, breaking into the store of happiness that your sweet summons had enriched me with ... O poor Calisto, deceived by your own servants! O deceitful Celestina, why did you not leave me to die instead of reviving my hopes and feeding the fires that now devour me? Why did you bring me a false message from my mistress? Why did you lead me to destruction with your lies? What purpose had you in sending me here, only to learn of her dislike, disfavour, distrust, and hatred from the lips of her who holds the keys of my damnation or my glory? You are my enemy. Did you not tell me that my mistress favoured me? Did you not tell me that she had summoned this prisoner here, of her own free will, not in order to banish me once more from her presence, but to end my banishment which by a previous command she had decreed? Whom can I trust? Where can I find truth? Is there anyone without guile? Is there any place free of deceivers? Who is my open enemy? Who is my true friend? Where is no treachery to be found? Who dared to plant this cruel and fatal hope in me?

MELIBEA: Stop, my lord. Your complaints are just. But my heart cannot bear them, nor can my eyes conceal my feelings. You weep out of sadness because you think me cruel. I weep out of pleasure at finding you so constant. O my dear lord and only joy, how much happier I should be if I could see your face as well as hear your voice! But since this is all we can do at present, accept the truth of the message I sent you by that faithful messenger. I confirm all that I said, and I promise you I meant it. Dry your eyes, sir, and command me as you please.

CALISTO: O my lady, my hope of glory, comfort, and relief of my pain, joy of my heart! What words would suffice to give you just thanks for the sublime and incomparable favour that you have done me at this moment of my extreme anguish, by permitting a weak and undeserving man to enjoy your sweet love? For although I have greatly desired it, contemplating your nobility, viewing your high estate, considering your perfection, contemplating your beauty, and comparing my small deserts with your high merits and perfect graces, your acclaimed and manifest virtues, I have always held myself unworthy to enjoy it. O mighty God, how can I fail to thank you for so wondrously performing your miracles on my behalf? Often in past days, when this thought came into my heart I banished it as impossible. But now, lady, the bright beams of your countenance have brought light to my eyes, warmed my heart, loosened my tongue, increased my worth, vanquished my cowardice, banished my irresolution, redoubled my strength, freed my numbed feet and hands, and, in brief, filled me with such courage that, drawn by their great power, I have risen to the sublime estate in which I now find myself, delightedly listening to your soft voice. Had I not known it and heard it before, I could never have believed that your sweet-scented words contained no deception. But now that I am certain of your sincerity I marvel and ask myself whether I am really Calisto to whom this miracle has happened.

MELIBEA: Ever since I knew who you are, my lord Calisto, your nobility and good looks have so affected me that you have not been out of my thoughts for a moment. I have striven for many days to conceal it. But when that woman recalled your sweet name to my mind, I could no longer hide my feelings. Therefore I have come to this place and at this hour to ask for your commands and to beg you to dispose of my person as you wish. A curse on these doors that stand between us and our delight! A curse on their strong locks and my weakness, but for which your complaints would cease and I should be happy.

CALISTO: What, my lady? Do you tell me to let mere planks prevent our pleasure? I thought that nothing but your will could stand in the way. Damned and troublesome doors, I would to God the hot fire that is consuming me would burn you! Even a third part of its strength would consume you utterly! In heaven's name, lady, let me call my servants to break them down.

PARMENO: D'you hear that, Sempronio? He wants to call us over, and that'll lead us into trouble. I don't like this visit at all. I think the affair has been unlucky from the start. I'm not staying here any longer.

SEMPRONIO: St, st! Listen! She won't let him call us over.

MELIBEA: Do you want to destroy me, my love, and ruin my reputation? Don't be headstrong. Our hopes are certain, and we need wait no longer than you decide. You only feel your own pain, I feel for both of us. You only feel your own grief, I feel yours as well as mine. Be content to come tomorrow night at the same hour over the garden wall. If you were to break down these cruel doors, even if we weren't discovered now, there'd be a terrible suspicion in my father's house tomorrow. And as you know, the greater the sinner the greater the sin. So the suspicion of my guilt would be known to the whole city immediately.

SEMPRONIO: This is a bad night's business for us! We shall be here till dawn, to judge by the time our master is taking, and even if luck's on our side, we shall be noticed before that either by Melibea's people or by the neighbours.

PARMENO: I've been begging you to leave for the last two hours. I said we were in for trouble.

CALISTO: O my lady and all my joy, why do you call it a sin when God's own saints have answered my prayers? I was praying before the altar in the Magdalene, when that kind old woman brought me your message yesterday.

PARMENO: You're raving, Calisto, you're raving! I swear to you, brother, he's no Christian. He says that what this old bitch brought about with her pestilential spells was the work of God's saints. And trusting in that, he wants to break down the doors. At the first blow Pleberio's servants will hear him, for they sleep near by, and then he'll be caught.

SEMPRONIO: Don't worry about that. We're not very near, and we can take to our heels the moment we hear a noise. Let him be. If he does something foolish, he'll pay the penalty.

PARMENO: You're right. You read my thoughts. So be it. But let's not get killed, we're too young. It's not cowardice but a natural thing to try to avoid killing or being killed. These servants of Pleberio's are madmen. They enjoy quarrelling and fighting better than food and sleep. And we should be crazier still if we waited to meet an enemy that loves brawling and feuds even more than outright victory. Oh, how you'd laugh, brother, if you could see me now!

I've half turned away, my legs are wide apart, my left foot's foremost ready to run, my coat's tucked in my belt and my shield's rolled up under my arms, so as not to get in my way. My God, I'm so scared I think I could run like a deer!

SEMPRONIO: I'm even better prepared. I've got my shield and sword strapped together so that they don't fall when I run, and my helmet in my hood.

PARMENO: What about the stones you had in it?

SEMPRONIO: I've thrown them out, so as to move faster. This breastplate you made me wear is heavy enough. I ought to have refused, it's too heavy to run in. Listen, listen! D'you hear, Parmeno? There's something wrong. That's finished us. Off you go! Make for Celestina's house, in case they try to cut us off from our own.

PARMENO: Run! Run! How slow you are! Poor sinner that I am! If they gain on us, drop your shield and everything.

SEMPRONIO: I wonder if they've killed our master?

PARMENO: I don't know. Don't talk. Just run and spare your breath. He's the least of my worries.

SEMPRONIO: Here, here, Parmeno! Come back, come back quietly. It's only the watch clattering down the next street.

PARMENO: Make quite sure. Don't trust your eyes, for they often make mistakes. I hadn't a drop of blood left in my body. I felt that my death was upon me and they were already raining blows on my back. I don't think I've ever been so frightened in my life, or in such a tight corner, though I've served in other men's houses for quite a long time and run into some troubles. I served the friars of Guadalupe for nine years, and we often used our fists. But I was never so afraid of being killed as I am tonight.

SEMPRONIO: Well, and haven't I served the priest of San Miguel, and the innkeeper in the square and the gardener Mollejas? And I had my fights with the boys who threw stones at the birds that perched in our big poplar tree and damaged the crops. But God help you if you're carrying arms. That's really dangerous. There's truth in the proverb, Loaded with iron, loaded with fear. But come back, come back, it certainly is the watch.

MELIBEA: Lord Calisto, what's that noise in the street? It sounds like people shouting and running away. Take care of yourself, for God's sake, you're in danger!

CALISTO: Don't be afraid, my lady, I've taken all precautions. It must be my men. They're madmen and disarm anyone who passes. It was probably someone they were chasing.

MELIBEA: Have you many men with you?

CALISTO: No, only two. But if they had six men against them, they'd have no trouble in disarming them and chasing them away. They're brave fellows, madam, picked men. I didn't hire them just for tonight. If it wasn't for your reputation, they would have smashed the doors to splinters. And if we had been overheard, they'd quickly have rid us of all your father's men.

MELIBEA: Oh, for heaven's sake, don't attempt any such thing! But I'm very glad you have such faithful men with you. Brave servants like that deserve all the food you give them. Treat them well, I beg you, sir, since Nature has given them such qualities, and reward them too, so that they keep your secrets. And if you punish them for their boldness and brawling, be kind to them afterwards. Then their bravery won't be daunted by your correction and they'll know how to be bold at the right time.

PARMENO: Come away, sir, come away! Come quickly. There's a crowd of men advancing with torches. You'll be seen and recognized, for you've nowhere to hide.

CALISTO: Oh, how unlucky I am, lady! I am compelled to leave you. Only fear for your honour, I swear, would make me go, not fear of death. May angels stay and guard you! I will come, as you commanded, through the garden.

MELIBEA: So be it, and God go with you.

*

PLEBERIO: Wife, wife! Are you asleep?

ALISA: No, my lord.

PLEBERIO: Can't you hear a noise in our daughter's room?

ALISA: Yes, I can . . . Melibea, Melibea!

PLEBERIO: She can't hear you. I'll call louder. Daughter! Melibea!

MELIBEA: What is it, my lord?

PLEBERIO: Who was walking and making a noise in your room?

MELIBEA: It was Lucrecia, my lord. She went to fetch me a jug of water because I was thirsty.

PLEBERIO: Go to sleep, daughter. I thought it was something else.

LUCRECIA: It doesn't take much noise to wake them. They sounded scared.

MELIBEA: The mildest creature becomes fierce when it's frightened for its dear young. What would they have done if they'd known that really I went down?

*

CALISTO: Shut the door, boys. And you, Parmeno, fetch a candle.

SEMPRONIO: You ought to get some rest, sir, and sleep for what remains of the night.

CALISTO: I will, for I certainly need it. Now what do you think, Parmeno, of the old lady you maligned so? What a good job she's done! And how badly we should have fared without her!

PARMENO: I didn't realize how much you were suffering, or that Melibea is so lovely that she's worth it all. So you shouldn't blame me. For I did know Celestina and her tricks, and it was my duty as your servant to warn you. But now she seems a changed woman. She's given them all up.

CALISTO: Greatly changed!

PARMENO: Yes, so changed that if I hadn't seen it I should never have believed it. But it's as true as you're alive.

CALISTO: Did you two hear my conversation with my mistress? What were you doing? Were you afraid?

SEMPRONIO: Afraid, sir? I assure you the whole world wouldn't have been enough to make us afraid. You wouldn't have found us afraid! We were waiting for you, sir, all ready and with our swords in our hands.

CALISTO: Did you snatch any sleep?

SEMPRONIO: Sleep, sir? Are we the boys to sleep? By God, I never sat down, nor so much as put my feet together. I kept looking in all directions, so that if anything came I could quickly leap to your help and do my best to protect you. And Parmeno here, though you may think he hasn't always been eager in your service, was as glad when he saw those torches as a wolf when he scents a flock of sheep. He was going to snatch them out of their hands, but he saw there were too many of them.

CALISTO: You needn't be surprised. He's foolhardy by nature. If he hadn't done it for me he'd have done it just the same. Men like him can't break with their habits. A vixen may shed her coat, she can't shed her nature. I told my mistress Melibea what kind of fellows you are, and how safe I was with you two at my back to protect me. I'm very much obliged to you, my boys. Pray God to keep you sound for I'll reward your good services more fully later on. Go now. God be with you, and sleep well.

PARMENO: Where shall we go, Sempronio? To bed and sleep or to eat in the kitchen?

SEMPRONIO: Go where you like. As for me, I'm going to see Celestina before daybreak to get my share of that chain. She's a tricky old whore, and I don't want to give her time to invent some excuse for cheating us.

PARMENO: You're right. I'd forgotten that. Let's go together, and if she tries any tricks we'll give her a scare that'll make her sorry. There's no friendship when money's at stake.

*

SEMPRONIO: Hush, hush! She sleeps just near this window. . . . (*Knocks*) Madam Celestina, open the door.

CELESTINA: Who's knocking?

SEMPRONIO: Your boys. Open up.

CELESTINA: I've no boys that go about at these hours.

SEMPRONIO: Open up! It's Parmeno and Sempronio. We've come to have breakfast with you.

CELESTINA: You crazy rogues! Come in, come in! What brings you here at this hour? It's almost dawn. What have you been doing? What's happened to you? Has Calisto spoilt his chances, or is he still hoping? How do things stand?

SEMPRONIO: How indeed, Mother? If it hadn't been for us, his soul would now be looking for its final lodging. If a true reckoning could be made of all that he owes us his whole estate wouldn't be enough to pay his debt. That is if what they say is true, and a man's life and person are worth more than anything else he has.

CELESTINA: Gracious, what a fight you must have had! Tell me about it, for goodness sake.

SEMPRONIO: Yes, such a fight, let me tell you, that my blood still boils in my veins only to think of it.

CELESTINA: Be calm, for goodness sake, and tell me.

PARMENO: You're asking too much. We're still tired and shaken by the row we've been in. You'd do better to prepare us some breakfast. It might calm us down a bit. I'm in no humour, let me tell you, to meet anyone who wants peace. I wish I could find someone now to vent my rage on, because I couldn't do it on the men who provoked us. They ran away too quickly.

CELESTINA: Damned if you don't frighten me, you look so fierce! But I think you're mocking me. Sempronio, tell me truly what happened.

SEMPRONIO: By God, I'm quite wild with rage. I can't control my anger and fury even with you, or remember you're a woman. But I've never used my strength against the weak. My cuirass, madam, is all hacked to pieces; my shield has lost its heft, my sword's as jagged as a saw, and my helmet is in my hood, all dented. Now I've nothing left with which to protect my master when he needs me to escort him, and he's arranged to go and see his lady tonight in the garden. How am I to buy new arms? I couldn't lay hands on a farthing to save my life.

CELESTINA: Ask your master to give you new arms, boy, since your old ones were spoilt in his service. You know that he'll agree at once, for he's not the sort of man who says, Live with me and find someone to keep you. He's generous enough to give you the money for that and more besides.

SEMPRONIO: Ah, but Parmeno's arms are ruined too. It'd cost his whole fortune to re-equip us both. How can you expect us to bother him by asking more of him than he'll willingly give – which is quite a lot? I won't have it said of me that when they grant me an inch I want an ell. He's already given us a hundred gold pieces and his chain as well. Another gift like that and he won't have a penny to bless himself with. This business must be costing him a lot. Let's be satisfied with what's reasonable, and not utterly ruin him by demanding more. If you grasp too much it slips through your fingers.

CELESTINA: The fool's being funny! Bless my old bones, if it were only a question of feeding ourselves, I'd say that we'd all done pretty well. But are you in your right mind, Sempronio? What's your reward got to do with my fee, your wages with my reward? Am I compelled to pay for your weapons, to make good what you lack? I'll be damned if you haven't caught me up on a trivial word I said to you the other day as we were walking in that street – that anything I possessed was yours, and that if ever I could do anything with my small strength you should never go short, and that if God should give me some profit from your master you shouldn't lose by it. But you know very well, Sempronio, those politenesses and affectionate protestations aren't binding. All is not gold that glitters. If it were, gold would be worth less. Tell me, Sempronio, haven't I guessed what was in your mind? I may be old, but I can still read your thoughts, you see. I'm very sorry, my boy, really I am. It's almost more than I can bear. But when I got back from your house, I gave the chain to that crazy girl Elicia to play with, and I don't know where she put it. Neither of us could catch a wink of sleep all night, we were so upset, not because of the value of the chain, which wasn't worth much, but because of her carelessness and my bad luck. Some friends and acquaintances of mine came in just after I did, and I'm afraid they must have pinched it, on the principle that finding's keeping.

But let me say to you lads now, if your master gave me anything, you can reckon I shall keep it. I didn't ask you for a share in your brocaded doublet, Sempronio, nor do I want one. Let's all serve him, and he'll reward each of us as we deserve. He gave me what he did because I risked my life for him twice. I've got more dents in my armour through serving him than you have, and I've put more into it. You must remember, my lads, that I've spent money and devoted my skill, which wasn't acquired by idling, as your mother could bear witness, Parmeno, God rest her soul.

I worked for this reward, and you must work for yours. I earned it by exercising my profession, while you have just been enjoying yourselves. You can't expect the same payment for your amusement as I get for my hard labours. But don't be depressed. Despite what I've said, if the chain turns up I'll give you both a pair of scarlet breeches, which look very smart on young men. But if it doesn't you must take the will for the deed, and I shall say nothing about my loss. I'm grateful to you both and fond of you for bringing me into this job. But if you're dissatisfied, so much the worse for you.

SEMPRONIO: This isn't the first time I've said that the vice of avarice is very prevalent among the old. When you were poor you were liberal. Now you're rich you're greedy. So avarice increases with wealth, and avarice leads to poverty, for nothing makes a miser poorer than riches. My goodness! The more he has the more he seems to need. This old woman said that I could take all the profit of this job, if I wanted to! That was when she thought there wouldn't be much. But now that she sees there is, she refuses to part with anything. She's following the children's proverb: If it's a little you get a bit, but if it's plenty you get nothing.

PARMENO: Either she gives us what she promised, or we take the lot from her. I've told you often enough what this old witch is like. It's a pity you didn't believe me.

CELESTINA: You may be angry with yourselves or your

master, or because your armour's ruined, but don't take it out on me! I know what's at the bottom of all this. I know where the shoe pinches. It's not because you need money, or even out of greed that you're asking me for what you do. It's because you're afraid I shall keep you tied hand and foot to Elicia and Areusa for the rest of your lives and never get you any other girls. That's why you're threatening me about the money, that's why you're trying to frighten me into sharing it out. But don't worry. If I procured these two for you I can procure you ten more, now that you have more experience, and there's more reason and merit on your side. And when I make a promise I keep it, as Parmeno can testify. Tell him, Parmeno, don't be shy, what happened the other night when Areusa had the belly-ache.

SEMPRONIO (*to Parmeno*): Tell her to go and pull down her breeches. I haven't come to hear about that.... (*To Celestina*) Don't try and put us off. This sort of thing doesn't wash with me. Let's have no more arguments. You can't take an old dog in like this. Count us out our two shares of what you got from Calisto, if you don't want to be shown up for what you are, and take your fine words elsewhere, old woman.

CELESTINA: Who do you think I am, Sempronio? A trull you picked up in a whorehouse? Hold your tongue and don't insult my white hairs. I am an old woman as God made me, and no worse than the rest. I live by my trade as any tradesman does, and very honestly too. I don't go pestering people who don't come to me. They come to my house to fetch me, they come and find me there. God can look into my heart, he knows whether I live well or ill. Don't come visiting your anger on me. There's justice for everyone. All are equal before the law, and though I'm only a woman I shall get as good a hearing as you in your fine clothes. Leave me alone in my own house to do as I like. And you, Parmeno, don't imagine you've got me in your power because you know my secrets and my past life, and all the misfortunes that happened to me and your poor mother. God forbid she should ever have served me a trick like this!

PARMENO: Don't shove those memories in my teeth, or I may send you to join her and make your complaints to her in person.

CELESTINA: Elicia, Elicia, get up now, and fetch me my cloak. Quickly! By all the saints in heaven, I'm going for the law, and I'll shout at them like a madwoman till they come. A fine thing! Threatening me in my own house. D'you think you've got a tame sheep to blackguard and bully, or a tethered hen? No, just an old woman of seventy. Go and pick a quarrel with men like yourselves, who wield the sword, not the distaff. Only cowards attack women and children and defenceless people. The foul flies only sting thin weak cattle, and barking curs always snap most fiercely at poor people's heels. If that girl up on the bed had listened to me our house wouldn't have been without a man last night, and we should have slept longer this morning. But as she waited for you and wanted to be faithful to you, you find us alone and unprotected. You certainly wouldn't be talking to us like this or making these demands if we had a man in the house. Anger and fury, as they say, soon yield to a stout adversary.

SEMPRONIO: Your throat's gasping for money, you old miser! Won't you be content with a third share of our winnings?

CELESTINA: A third share? Clear out of my house! And don't you shout, Parmeno, or you'll rouse the neighbours. And don't drive me too far, either, if you don't want your affairs and Calisto's to be known all over the town.

SEMPRONIO: Scream as loud as you like. Either you keep your promise, or this is your last hour.

ELICIA: For God's sake put that sword away. Hold him, hold him, Parmeno! Don't let that madman kill her!

CELESTINA: Justice, justice, neighbours, call the watch! Justice! These ruffians are killing me in my own house.

SEMPRONIO: Ruffians? Call us what you like! But just you wait, my lady witch, and I'll send you to hell with your passport.

CELESTINA: Oh, they're killing me! Oh, oh! A confessor, let me confess!

PARMENO: Strike her, strike her! Finish her off as you've begun, or someone will hear us. Kill her, kill her! One enemy the less!

CELESTINA: Let me confess!

ELICIA: You wicked man! May you be damned for this! Look what you've done. You've killed my mother, my only comfort!

SEMPRONIO: Run, run, Parmeno! There's a crowd coming. Look out, look out! Here's the watch!

PARMENO: Oh, I'm a poor sinner! There's nowhere for us to run. They've blocked the door.

SEMPRONIO: Better jump out of this window than die at the hands of the law.

PARMENO: Jump and I'll follow you.

Act Thirteen

Calisto wakes up and talks to himself. After a while he calls Tristan and his other servants, and then falls asleep again. Tristan is standing at the door when Sosia arrives in tears. In answer to Tristan's questions he tells him that Sempronio and Parmeno are dead. They take the news to Calisto, who laments bitterly on hearing it.

CALISTO: How well I've slept after that honeyed visit, that heavenly conversation! I am completely rested. Was it my happiness that gave me such repose? Was it physical exercise that caused me to sleep so long – or was it the glorious exaltation of my spirit? I shouldn't be surprised if it was both together that sealed my eyelids, for I toiled with body and mind last night, and rejoiced in spirit and senses. Sadness most certainly gives rise to thoughts, and much thought prevents sleep, as with me in these past few days when I doubted whether I should ever attain the blessing that I now possess. O my love, O my lady Melibea! What are you thinking now? Are you sleeping or awake? Are you thinking of me or another? Are you up or still in bed? How happy and fortunate is Calisto if what happened was not really a dream! Did I dream it or not? Was it a fantasy or was it real? But I was not alone, my servants were with me, two of them. If they say it really happened, I shall have to believe them. I will send for them to confirm my happiness. Tristan, boy! Tristan, get up there!

TRISTAN: I am getting up, sir.

CALISTO: Go quickly and fetch Sempronio and Parmeno.

TRISTAN: Straight away, sir.

Sigh no more, sad lover,
  Now your cares depart.
Sleep and take your rest,
  You have won the heart
Of her for whom you sighed.
  See Melibea yield,
Pain gives place to joy,
Sorrow quits the field.

TRISTAN: There's not a servant in the house.

CALISTO: Open the shutters then, and see what the time is.

TRISTAN: It's broad daylight, sir.

CALISTO: Then close them again, and let me sleep till dinner time.

TRISTAN: I'll go down to the door and see that no one disturbs my master's sleep. If anyone comes for him, I'll turn him away. Oh, what's all that shouting in the market-place? What can it be? Perhaps there's an execution, or the people have got up early to run the bulls. I can't think why there should be such a commotion. Here comes Sosia, the stable-boy. He'll tell me what it is. The rascal's all dishevelled. He must have been brawling in some tavern. If my master sees him in this state, he'll have him soundly beaten. The boy may be crazy, but a beating will bring him to his senses. He seems to be crying. What's the matter, Sosia? Why are you crying? Where have you been?

SOSIA: Oh, alas, alas! The terrible loss! And what a dishonour to my master's house! It's a black day for us. Oh, poor lads, poor lads!

TRISTAN: What is it? What's the matter? What's upset you so! Why is it a black day?

SOSIA: Sempronio and Parmeno...!

TRISTAN: What about Sempronio and Parmeno? What's all this, you idiot? Explain yourself. You're frightening me.

SOSIA: Our comrades, our brothers...!

TRISTAN: Either you're drunk, or you're crazy, or you're bringing bad news? Why don't you tell me what it is? What are you saying about the lads?

SOSIA: They've been beheaded in the square.

TRISTAN: A terrible thing for us, if it's true! Did you see it for yourself or did someone tell you?

SOSIA: They were nearly dead already. But one of them, when he saw me there weeping, pulled himself together and gave me a look. He raised his hands, as if in thanks to God and to ask me if I were not sorry for his death. Then he lowered his head in sad farewell, and the tears fell from his eyes, as if to say that we should never meet again till Judgement Day.

TRISTAN: You misunderstood. He must have been trying to ask you whether Calisto was there. But you've given me enough proof. It's a dreadful misfortune indeed. Let's hurry to our master, and break the sad news to him.

SOSIA: Master! Master!

CALISTO: What is it, you idiots? Didn't I tell you not to wake me?

SOSIA: Wake up and get up! If you don't protect your servants, we're all done for! Sempronio and Parmeno have been beheaded in the square as public malefactors, after a proclamation of their crime.

CALISTO: God help me! What's this you're saying? This news comes so suddenly that I don't know whether to believe it. Did you see them, boy?

SOSIA: Yes, I did.

CALISTO: Mind now what you're saying. They were with me only last night.

SOSIA: Well, they got up early enough to die.

CALISTO: Oh, my faithful servants! You followed me most loyally, you advised and assisted me like true men. Can this really be true? It's a bad thing for me. I am dishonoured for life. What will become of me now that I've lost such a pair of servants? Tell me, in heaven's name, Sosia, what was the reason? What did the proclamation say? Where were they executed? What judge was responsible?

SOSIA: Sir, the executioner proclaimed the reason for their death. 'Justice ordains death for brutal murder.' That's what he shouted.

CALISTO: Who did they kill so suddenly? What's behind all this? They only said good night to me four hours ago. Who was it they killed?

SOSIA: A woman called Celestina, sir.

CALISTO: What's that you say?

SOSIA: Didn't you hear me, sir?

CALISTO: If this is true, kill me now and I'll forgive you. It's worse than you know, worse even than you can imagine, if it was Celestina, the old woman with the scar, that they murdered.

SOSIA: It certainly was. I saw her lying in her house, stabbed all over, and a young servant crying over her.

CALISTO: Poor lads! Tell me, how did they die? Did they see you? And speak to you?

SOSIA: Oh, if you'd seen them, sir, your heart would have broken with sorrow. One of them was senseless, with his brains knocked out, and the other had both his arms broken and his face smashed in. They were both covered with blood. They'd jumped from a high window to escape the watch. So they were almost dead when they beheaded them, and I don't think they felt anything.

CALISTO: But I feel my honour wounded. Would to God I were in their place and had lost my life rather than my honour and all my hopes of completing the enterprise I've begun! That's what hurts me most about this dreadful business. It's unlucky for me. My name and reputation will be bandied from mouth to mouth, and my deepest secrets will be traded through the squares and markets. What will become of me? Where shall I go? It's no good going to the square. They're dead and I can't help them. But what if I stay here? It'll look like cowardice. Whose advice can I ask? Tell me, Sosia, why did they kill her?

SOSIA: Sir, that servant of hers who was weeping for her death shouted it out for everyone to hear. She said that it was because she wouldn't give them a share in a gold chain that you gave her.

CALISTO: A sad day for me! And a tribulation indeed! My possessions pass from hand to hand and my reputation from mouth to mouth. Everything will become known: all that I said to her and to them, all that they know about me, and the business in which they were engaged. I shall not dare to appear in public. O unlucky lads, to come to such a sudden end! My happiness is vanishing. It's an old proverb that the higher one climbs the greater one's fall. I gained much last night, and today I've lost all my gains. Calm days at sea are rare. I was all set for happiness, if only fate could have stilled the rough winds that have overwhelmed me. Fortune has been against me everywhere and in every way. But however cruelly my household is persecuted, however great my own ill luck, I must bear misfortune with equanimity. That is the test of a brave heart. There's no better touchstone by which a man may prove the quality of his virtue or courage. So whatever hurt or evil may come to me, I will not fail to obey the command of her for whose sake all this has happened. For I shall achieve more by gaining the glory I hope for than these dead men have lost by their death. They were bold and domineering, and sooner or later they would have paid for it. The old woman was a wicked cheat, as is clear from her dealings with them, and they quarrelled over the division of the spoils. It was the will of God that she should die like this in payment for the many adulteries that were committed under her auspicies. I'll tell Sosia and young Tristan to get ready. They shall escort me on the road I long to travel. They must take ladders, for the walls are high. Tomorrow I will see what can be done to avenge my men's deaths; and if I can do nothing I'll defend my innocence by pleading that I was out of town. Or I will pretend to be mad, the better to enjoy the sweet delights of my love, as that great captain Ulysses did to escape the Trojan war and stay with his wife Penelope.

Act Fourteen

Melibea is talking to Lucrecia. She is greatly distressed that Calisto has not come though he agreed to pay her a visit that night. He keeps his promise and comes accompanied by Sosia and Tristan. After he has had his desire, all three return home, and Calisto shuts himself in his room, lamenting that he was with Melibea only for such a short time. He begs Phoebus to veil his light so that he may once more enjoy his desires.

MELIBEA: The gentleman we are waiting for is very late. What do you think can have delayed him, Lucrecia?

LUCRECIA: I think there must be a good reason, madam, something unavoidable must have detained him.

MELIBEA: May the angels guard him, and keep him out of danger! I am not so much worried by his lateness as by imagining all the things that might have happened to him between his house and here. Perhaps he decided to come to his rendezvous in disguise, the way young men do when they go out late, and has been stopped by the night watch. They would not have recognized him and might have attacked him. Then he might have struck back to defend himself, and they might have beaten him. Or perhaps the watchdogs have bitten him. They are no respecters of persons and would not know the difference between a visitor and a thief. Or perhaps he has fallen into a gutter or a hole and hurt himself. Oh dear, what disasters this love of mine conjures up, and how my tormenting imagination magnifies them! God grant that none of these things may have happened. I'd rather he stayed away as long as . . . But listen, listen! I hear footsteps in the street, and I think I can hear talking on the other side of the wall.

SOSIA: Set up the ladder, Tristan. This is the best place although it's high.

TRISTAN: Climb up, sir, and I'll come over with you. For we don't know who may be in the garden. There are people talking.

CALISTO: Stay here, you idiots. I shall go alone. I can hear it's my mistress.

MELIBEA: Your servant rather, and your captive, who prizes your life above her own. O my lord, don't jump from so high, or I shall die watching you. Come down the ladder slowly. Don't be in such a hurry.

CALISTO: Angelic creature! Precious pearl beside whom all the world looks ugly! My mistress, my glory, I cannot believe that I hold you in my arms. I am so confused with delight that I cannot feel all the joy I possess.

MELIBEA: My lord, I gave myself into your hands because I wanted to obey you. But do not treat me worse for pitying you than if I had been proud and pitiless. Do not destroy me so quickly to gain a brief pleasure. Wrongs once done are more easily repented than set right. Enjoy the pleasure I enjoy, the sight and presence of my lover. Do not ask or take what once taken you can never return.

CALISTO: I have risked my whole life, my lady, to gain this favour. How could I renounce it when it is in my grasp? You would not command me to hold back, nor could I prevail on myself to do so. Don't ask me to be so faint-hearted. No man worthy of the name would restrain himself now, especially one who loves you as I do. I have sailed these hot seas of desire for so long. Will you not let me come to my sweet haven and rest from my long labours?

MELIBEA: Speak as much as you like, but I beg you to keep your hands from straying. Be still, sir. Since I am yours, be satisfied with outward favours, which are the proper fruit of lovers, don't try to rob me of the greatest gift that Nature has given me. Remember that a good shepherd should shear his flock, but not poison and corrupt it.

CALISTO: But why, lady? Why will you not satisfy my desire? Do you want me to go on suffering? Do you want me to begin this game all over again? Pardon my shameless hands, lady, which never thought themselves worthy to touch even your garments but now delight to find your sweet body and lovely, delicate limbs.

MELIBEA: Go further off, Lucrecia.

CALISTO: Why, madam? I am happy to have such a witness of my joy.

MELIBEA: I want no witness of my shame. If I had thought that you would treat me so outrageously I should never have entrusted myself to you.

SOSIA: D'you hear what they're saying, Tristan? I think things are going well.

TRISTAN: To judge by what I've heard, my master's the luckiest man born. But by my life, young though I am, I could give as good an account of myself as he!

SOSIA: With a treasure like that anyone could prove his mettle. But he'll have to pay the piper, and it's costing him a good deal. Two servants have gone into the making of this sauce already.

TRISTAN: He's forgotten them by now. You can get yourself killed serving these scoundrels. You act like a madman, expecting them to defend you, and then ... Take service with the Count, my father used to advise me, but never kill. There they are, happy in each other's arms while his servants lie shamefully beheaded.

MELIBEA: O my lord and my life, how could you have ravished me of my virgin's name and crown for a pleasure so quickly over? O my poor mother, if you knew what has happened, how gladly would you die yourself or even kill me! Then you would be the cruel executioner of your own child, and I the sad cause of your death. O my honoured father, I have besmirched your good name and caused the ruin of your house! And you, my betrayer, why did I not see the evil that would come from admitting you and the danger that threatened me?

SOSIA: I should like to be the one listening to her prattle. They all recite the same litany, when the deed's done and can't be undone. But that idiot Calisto's taking it seriously.

CALISTO: Dawn's about to break. But how can that be? We don't seem to have been here more than an hour, and yet the clock's striking three.

MELIBEA: O my dear lord, since everything is now yours, and I am your mistress and you can't deny my love, do not stay away. On such nights as you will, come at this same hour to this same private place, I shall always be waiting for you. For now I know what delight I can expect on future nights. But for the present, God be with you. I don't think you'll be seen, for it's still quite dark, nor will they hear me in the house, since dawn has not yet broken.

CALISTO: Set up the ladder, boys.

SOSIA: It's in place, sir. Climb down.

MELIBEA: Come here, Lucrecia. I'm alone. My lord has gone away, taking my heart with him and leaving me his. Did you hear us?

LUCRECIA: No, madam, I have been asleep.

SOSIA: We must go quietly, Tristan. For this is the hour when rich men rise, and men greedy for worldly goods, and worshippers in churches, monasteries, and chapels, and lovers like our master, and workers in the fields and farms. This is the hour when shepherds drive their ewes into the folds to give suck. If a passer-by were to hear anything, his honour and Melibea's would be smirched.

TRISTAN: What a simple lad you are! You say that we should

be quiet, and then you speak her name. You'd make a fine leader to guide men through Moorish country at night! You advise one thing and do the opposite, you reveal what you want to hide, you damage what you want to preserve, you say 'be quiet' and shout at the top of your voice, you ask a question and provide your own answer. Since you're such a clever one, perhaps you'll tell me in which month the fifth of August falls. Then we shall know if we have enough hay to feed you this year.

CALISTO: I am worried, but my worries are not yours. Come home quietly, or they may hear us in the house. Shut the door, and we'll take some rest. I want to be alone in my room. I'll take off my own cuirass. Go to bed, both of you.

Alas, alas! How agreeable to my nature are solitude, silence, and darkness! But what can be the reason? Is it because I remember my treachery in leaving that lady, whom I love so much, before daylight? Or is it from grief at my dishonour? Alas, it is. I feel the wound now that it is cold, now that my blood has cooled which was warm yesterday, now that I see the gap in my household, the loss of my servants, the wastage of my patrimony, the disrepute into which I have fallen. For their execution has brought me into disgrace. What have I done? What have I come to? Why did I not appear at once in fury, and take proud and swift vengeance for the patent wrong I had suffered? O miserable charm of this most transient life, why is a man so greedy for it that rather than die at once he will prefer to live on in disgrace for one year more, which will destroy all the reputation he has gained in the past? And even then he has no certainty of the next hour or even the next minute. There's no postponing our debts, we are always compelled to pay at once. Why did I not go out immediately to discover the hidden cause of my public disgrace? How brief is the joy of this world! Its pleasures are costly and transient.

Repentance is a good deal cheaper. Alas, how can my great loss ever be made good? What shall I do? Where can I turn for advice? Whom can I tell of my disaster? Why do I conceal it from my family and my other servants? I'm in trouble abroad, and I don't speak of it at home. I had better put in an appearance. But if I do, it's too late to protest that I was present, and too soon to deny it. I need time to recruit friends and old servants, relatives and clients, and to collect arms and other means of vengeance.

O cruel judge, this is a poor repayment for the bread you have eaten at my father's table! I thought that with your protection I could kill a thousand men without fear of punishment. But you're a foul cheat, an enemy of truth, a low-born villain. They're right when they say that you were made a judge because there were no good men. You should have remembered that you and the men you condemned were once comrades, since you all served my family. But when a mean man gets rich, he has no relatives or friends. Who would have thought that it was you who would destroy me? Truly, no one can do more harm than an unsuspected enemy. Thanks to you they will say of me that I fetched from the forest the wood that has burnt me and reared the crow that has pecked out my eye. You proclaimed your sins in public, but have executed men who concealed theirs. Yet everyone knows that a secret crime is less heinous than a public one, since it has less effect, as the laws of Athens say, which are not written in blood. On the contrary, according to them it's better to pardon the criminal than punish the innocent. It's dangerous to defend a righteous cause before an unrighteous judge. And how much more dangerous for my poor servants, who weren't innocent! Remember if a man has sinned, he has advocates in heaven and on earth. So God and the king will hold you guilty and I will be your enemy for life. How could one man be held guilty of another man's crime? Yet only because those two were together you executed them both. But what am I saying? To whom am I speaking? Have I lost my senses? What is this, Calisto? Were you dreaming? Are you asleep or awake? Are you standing or lying down? Look, you're in your own room. The offender isn't here. Who are you quarrelling with? Come into your right mind. Remember that the absent are never in the right. Hear both parties before you pronounce sentence. Don't you know that if you're to execute justice you must not consider friendship or obligation or kinship? Have you forgotten that all men are equal before the law? Think of Romulus, the founder of Rome, who killed his own brother because he transgressed it. Think of the Roman Torquatus who executed his son for disobeying an order of the tribunes. There are many similar cases. Reflect that if he had been here he would have answered that doers and accomplices deserve the same penalty, and that is why he ordered both to be executed for a crime that only one had committed, and that if he hurried the execution, the crime was notorious, and there was small need of proof since they were taken in the act of assassination, and that one was killed already by his fall. And I think he was urged to it also by the clamour of Celestina's maid, who was weeping there in the house. He wanted to avoid a commotion so as not to disgrace me, for my reputation would have been ruined if people had been about in time to hear the executioner's proclamation. He didn't wait, therefore, but had them executed very early, since in order to be legal the execution had to be proclaimed in this way. So if that is the explanation, I ought to be obliged and indebted to him for the rest of my life, not merely as an old servant of my father's but as a true brother. And supposing it isn't, supposing that everything was not done for a good purpose, remember, Calisto, the great joy you have just had, remember your mistress and your great good fortune. And since you hold your life cheap in her service, why care about the death of others, for no grief is equal to the joy you have received!

My lady and my life! I never thought to slight you in your absence. But I seem to be setting very little value on the favour you did me. I do not want to think angry thoughts or keep company with melancholy. O incomparable gift! O ineffable contentment! How could I pray God for any greater reward for my merits – if such exist on earth – than I have now received? Why am I not content? It's wrong for me to be dissatisfied with one who has given me such a gift. If I am ungrateful and fall into a fury I shall lose this great possession. I want no other honour or glory, no other wealth, no other father or mother, no other friends or relations. By day I will stay in my room, and at night in that sweet paradise, in that happy garden, among those gracious plants and that fresh verdure. O night of my relief, would you were here again! O shining Phoebus, hasten on your customary way! O lovely stars, come out before your habitual time! O slow-moving clock, would I could see you burnt with the sharp fires of love! If you expected the same joys as I at midnight, you would cease to obey the will of the craftsman who made you. And you winter months, that are still far off, come with your longer nights and substitute them for these endless days. It seems a year already since I saw that blessed comfort, that easer of my woes. But what am I demanding? What am I demanding, like an impatient fool? Something that never was and can never be. The course of nature cannot be changed. It will never depart from its law. Its revolutions are the same for all. All alike have their times to live and to die. There is a fixed period for the secret revolutions of the celestial firmament, the planets and the north star, and for the monthly waxing and waning of the moon. Heaven, earth, sea, fire, wind, heat, and cold, all things are governed by the same rein, driven by the same spur. What would it profit me that my iron clock struck twelve, if the heavenly clock did not agree? The dawn comes no sooner though you rise early.

But sweet imagination, to whom all is possible, hasten to my aid! Call to my mind the angelic presence of that bright form. Recall to my ears the soft sound of her words, those reluctant phrases that fell from her ruby lips: her 'Leave me, sir. Come no nearer', her 'Do not be discourteous', 'Do not contrive my ruin' – which she several times repeated – and her loving embraces between her words; the way she repelled me and then clasped me to her, fled away and came near, and her sweet kisses, and the last farewell with which she took leave of me. How it hurt her to speak it! How she stretched out her arms and wept unconscious tears that fell like pearls from her clear and shining eyes!

SOSIA: What shall we do about Calisto, Tristan? Hasn't he slept enough? It's four o'clock, and he hasn't called us or eaten anything.

TRISTAN: Leave him. There's no hurry to wake him. He's torn between grief for those two lads and joy for the great pleasure he has had with Melibea. It's not surprising that two such conflicting emotions should leave a weak man prostrated.

SOSIA: D'you think he's so grieved by their deaths? If that girl I can see outside weren't more grieved than he is, she wouldn't be wearing weeds of that colour.

TRISTAN: Who is she, brother?

SOSIA: Come over to the window and see her before she passes. You see the girl in black wiping the tears from her eyes? That's Elicia, Celestina's maid and Sempronio's mistress, a very pretty girl. But she's a lost soul now, because Celestina was like a mother to her and Sempronio was her chief lover. You see the house she's gone into. A beautiful woman lives there, fresh and charming and such a one for love that she's almost a whore. A man would be lucky if he could have her favours on the cheap. Her name's Areusa. I know she caused poor Parmeno many a sleepless night. But she'll be sorry for his death all the same.

Act Fifteen

Areusa is arguing with a ruffian called Centurio, who takes his leave when he hears Elicia coming. Elicia tells Areusa of the deaths caused by the love of Calisto and Melibea, and Areusa and Elicia agree that Centurio must avenge the three victims on the two lovers. Elicia leaves Areusa without agreeing to her request that they should live together, since she does not wish to give up the pleasures of her own house.

ELICIA: What can all this clamour be at my cousin's? If she has already heard the sad news I'm bringing her, I shall miss the first burst of grief that is one's reward for such a message. Weep, weep your bitter tears! You don't find men like those at every street-corner. I'm glad that she feels it so much. Let her tear her hair as I have done in my sorrow. Let her learn that to lose good friends is worse than death itself. I love her better than I did before, now that I've heard her grief!

AREUSA: Out of my house, you ruffian, you villain, you lying cheat! You've tricked and fooled me with your empty offers. With your wheedling and flattery you've robbed me of everything I possess. I have given you a doublet and cloak, a sword and buckler and shirts, two at a time, embroidered all over. I've given you arms and a horse, and placed you with a good master whose shoes you aren't fit to untie, you rogue. But now that I ask a single favour from you you find a thousand excuses.

CENTURIO: Ask me to kill ten men in your service, sister, but don't ask me to go a mile on foot.

AREUSA: What did you gamble away your horse for, you

dicing rogue? You'd have been hanged by now if it weren't for me. Three times I've got you out of the hands of the police, four times I've paid your debts at the tables. Why do I do it? Why am I such a fool? Why do I stay faithful to this poltroon? Why do I believe his lies? Why do I let him enter my door? What good is there in him? Curly hair, a scar on his face, twice whipped, maimed in his sword hand, and he keeps thirty whores in the brothel. Get out of here quick, and never let me see you again. Never speak to me or say that you know me, or by the bones of the father that engendered me and the mother that bore me, I will see you get a thorough thrashing on those humped shoulders of yours. And you know that I've got someone who'll do it, and no one will touch him.

CENTURIO: Rave away, you silly creature! But if I lose my temper someone will weep for it. Still, I'll put up with it and go, for someone's coming and I shouldn't like anyone to hear us.

ELICIA: I'll go in. It's not lamentations I heard but threats and quarrelling.

AREUSA: Oh dear dear! Is that you, Elicia darling? Jesus, Jesus, I can't believe my eyes. What's all this? What's made you so sad? Why are you in mourning? Truly you alarm me, sister. Tell me quickly what's the matter. I'm all upset. I haven't a drop of blood left in my body.

ELICIA: A terrible grief! A terrible loss! The sorrow I show is far less than what I feel inside. My heart's in deeper mourning than my cloak or my veil. Oh sister, sister, I can't speak. My voice is choking in my throat.

AREUSA: Oh dear Lord, how you frighten me! Tell me. Stop tearing your hair, and beating your breast. Is it something that affects us both? Has it anything to do with me?

ELICIA: O my dear cousin, my dear friend! Sempronio and Parmeno are no more. They've gone from the world. Their souls are purging their sins already. They're released from this sad life.

AREUSA: What are you saying? Don't tell me it's true. Don't tell me, for God's sake, or it'll kill me.

ELICIA: But it's worse than you've heard. Listen and I'll tell you something sadder still. Your old friend Celestina, Celestina whom I looked on as a mother, who spoiled and protected me, and made me feel the equal of anyone in the world, Celestina thanks to whom I was known throughout the city and the suburbs, is now making her last account. They slashed her all over before my very eyes; she was lying in my lap when they killed her.

AREUSA: Oh, what a terrible grief! Such news that one might die of weeping! A sudden disaster! An irreparable loss! How quickly Fortune's wheel has turned! Who killed them? How did they die? I'm astounded, overwhelmed. It seems impossible. Only a week ago I saw them alive, and now we must say, 'The Lord have mercy on their souls!' Tell me, darling, how this cruel disaster happened.

ELICIA: I will. You've heard, sister, about the love of Calisto and that crazy girl Melibea. You know that Sempronio engaged Celestina as go-between, and she was to be well paid for her trouble. Indeed she acted with such speed and diligence that she brought the thing off at the second asking. Well, when Calisto saw her succeed so quickly where he had so little hope, he gave my poor aunt, among other things, a gold chain. And as it's true of gold that the longer we live the more we covet it, finding herself rich, she clung to the whole of the profit in her wicked greed, refusing to give Sempronio and Parmeno a share, though they had agreed between them to divide whatever Calisto gave them. Well, they came back tired one morning after accompanying their master all night, and out of temper because of some brawl which they said they had been mixed up in. And they demanded their share in the chain to make good their damage. Celestina stoutly denied that there was any agreement or promise. She affirmed that all the winnings were hers, and went on to mention one or two little matters. For, as they say, once fish-wives start scolding ... They became furious because they were not only in great need – and necessity knows no friends – but angry and tired as well, which added fuel to their quarrel. What's more they saw all their hopes destroyed by her breaking her word. They did not know what to do and spent some time in discussion. Finally when they found her avariciously persisting in her refusal, they drew their swords and hacked and stabbed her to pieces.

AREUSA: Oh, the poor woman! To think that her old age should come to this! But what happened to them? How did they meet their ends?

ELICIA: As soon as they had committed the murder they leapt out of the window to escape the watch, that happened to be passing at the time. But they were arrested, half killed by their fall, and beheaded immediately.

AREUSA: O Parmeno, my love! What sorrow I feel for his death! I am sorry I fell so deeply in love with him so quickly, since our love was to be so short. But since the bad news has come, since the disaster has happened, and since their lives are lost and can't be restored by tears, don't be so distressed or you'll go blind with weeping. For I think your sorrow is only a little greater than mine, and you see how patiently I bear my loss.

ELICIA: I shall go mad. Poor wretch, I shall go out of my mind! No one can feel the sorrow that I do! No one has lost what I have lost. Oh, how much better and more honest my tears would have been for anyone else's loss than for my own! Where am I to go? I have lost my mother, my shield, and my protection. I have lost my friend, who would have been as good to me as a husband. O wise, honourable, and respected Celestina, how many of my lapses did you cover with your rare skill! You laboured and I enjoyed myself. You went out while I stayed at home. You wore rags so that I might be clothed. You returned home laden like a bee and I wasted your substance, for I knew no better. Worldly wealth and happiness, how little we value them while we have them! We only know their true value when we have lost them. O Calisto and Melibea, how many deaths you have caused! May your love come to a bad end and all your pleasures turn sour. May your joy turn to tears and your pleasures to pain. May the soft grasses on which you took your stolen delights turn to snakes, and your songs to tears. May the shady trees of that garden wither before your eyes, and its sweet-smelling flowers turn black.

AREUSA: Quietly, for God's sake, sister! Complain no more, stop your tears, dry your eyes, and come back to life. For when one door closes, Fortune generally opens another. And this wound will heal, cruel though it is. Things that can't be remedied can often be revenged. And in this case though you can't hope for a remedy vengeance is to hand.

ELICIA: On whom can we take vengeance? I grieve for her and I grieve for her murderers. Their punishment is as painful to me as the killing itself. But what do you want me to do? All the weight of this falls on me. Would to God I were with them and not left behind to weep for them all. But what grieves me most is that in spite of everything that unfeeling wretch goes every night to see and enjoy his foul Melibea; I'm sure she must be very proud that so much blood has been spilt in her honour.

AREUSA: In that case, on whom else should we take revenge? Those who ate the meal should pay the bill. Leave it to me. I'll follow them and see where they meet and when. As true as I'm the daughter of the old pastry-woman, whom you knew well, I'll track them down and turn their love into grief. I'll use the fellow you saw me quarrelling with when you came in, and I promise you he'll prove a crueller executioner to Calisto than Sempronio to Celestina. And he'll certainly be delighted to have me ask a service of him, for he went away very sad at the way I abused him. He'll think the heavens have opened when I speak to him again and send him to do my business. But tell me, sister, from whom can I inquire how they contrive their meetings, so that I can set a trap that will make Melibea weep as much as she's now rejoicing?

ELICIA: I know another of Parmeno's comrades, a stable-boy called Sosia, who accompanies his master every night. If I work on him I shall learn the whole secret, and that'll put us on our way to the revenge you talk of.

AREUSA: Do me the favour, cousin, of sending this Sosia to me. I'll talk to him, and flatter him and wheedle him till he's told me everything that has happened and everything that will. Then I'll make him and his master sorry for every pleasure they've enjoyed. But don't grieve, Elicia, dear soul. Bring your clothes and possessions to my house and live with me. You'd be very lonely there, and loneliness is a friend to grief. New loves will make you forget the old. The birth of a new child compensates for three that have died. Take a new lover and you'll regain the happy memories and vanished pleasures of the past. You shall have an equal share of every crumb in my larder. I'm sorrier for your distress than for the death of those who caused it. It's true that grief for one's losses is greater than the pleasure one feels in the expectation of something new, even if one's certain of it. But what's done can't be undone, and the dead can't be called back to life. Dead's dead, as the saying goes, but we go on with our lives. Leave the survivors to me, and I'll give them as bitter a draught as they've made you swallow. I may be young, cousin, but when I'm roused I know how to contrive a plot as well as anyone. May God avenge me on all my enemies as Centurio will on Calisto!

ELICIA: But be careful. I fear that even if I send Sosia to you the result won't be as you hope. His comrades have paid with their lives for talking too much; those who survive will keep quiet and reveal no secrets. I'm very grateful to you for inviting me to live with you. God preserve you and grant you all you need. You've proved that kinship is no hollow thing and can be trusted in adversity. But though I should like to accept, so as to have the pleasure of your sweet company, I cannot, for it would prejudice me too much. I don't have to explain myself, I know you understand me. I'm well known there, sister, and it's my parish. That house will always be called by poor Celestina's name, and all the girls who have followers and suitors, the friends and relations of those she looked after, always go there. They use the house for their assignations, and I shall make a little profit. Also the few friends I've still got wouldn't know where else to look for me. As you know, it's difficult to break a habit, and to change your ways is a sort of death, and a rolling stone gathers no moss. So I'd rather stay there if only because the rent is paid for this year; and I don't want to waste the money. True, none of these things would be enough in itself, but all together they help and benefit me. Now I think it's time for me to go. I'll look after what we talked about. God be with you. I'm off.

Act Sixteen

Imagining that their daughter Melibea is still a virgin – which, as we have seen, she is not – Pleberio and Alisa are discussing her marriage. She overhears their conversation, and is so distressed that she sends Lucrecia to interrupt them and force them to change the subject.

PLEBERIO: Alisa, my dear, time seems to be slipping through our fingers, as they say. The days flow by like the waters of a river. Nothing passes so quickly as life. Death follows us and hedges us in, and we are its neighbours, and soon we shall join its banner as nature decrees. We see this clearly enough when we look at our equals, our brothers and cousins all around us. The earth swallows them all; they are all in their eternal dwellings. And since we are uncertain when we shall be called, seeing such clear signs, we must gird up our loins and pick up our burdens in readiness for our enforced march. For we must not let death's cruel summons alarm us or take us by surprise. Let us prepare our souls in time, for forewarned is forearmed. Let us leave our property to our dear heir, and choose for our one daughter such a husband as our position entitles her to, so that we may leave this world calmly and contentedly. Now we must diligently put our plan into effect, and conclude the negotiations that we have already begun. I shouldn't like to be so negligent as to leave our daughter with guardians, for she will be better off with a house of her own than in ours. We must preserve her from scandal, for no virtue is so perfect as to escape slander and malice. Nothing preserves a girl's chaste reputation better than an early marriage. No one in the whole city would refuse an alliance with us. And would not any man be glad to marry such a jewel as Melibea? For she has the four principal qualities that men demand in a bride: first, modesty, honour, and virginity; secondly, beauty; thirdly, noble birth and parentage; and fourthly, wealth. Nature has endowed her with all these. And if any more is asked of us they will find that in her as well.

ALISA: God keep her safe, my lord Pleberio, so that we may see our desires fulfilled in our lifetime. But I don't think any man is worthy of our daughter. Considering your virtue and noble blood, there can't be many who deserve her. But this is a father's business and has nothing to do with the women. I will be pleased with whatever you decide, and our daughter will obey you chastely and humbly, as she has always lived.

LUCRECIA: If you knew what I do your hearts would break. Yes, truly they would. For the treasure's lost. Misfortunes await your old age! Calisto has taken the treasure, and there's no one left to mend virginities now that Celestina's dead. You've thought of this too late. You should have woken up sooner. Listen to them, listen, lady Melibea!

MELIBEA: What are you hiding there for, you silly girl?

LUCRECIA: Come over here, madam, and you'll hear how anxious your parents are to find you a husband.

MELIBEA: For goodness sake be quiet, or they'll hear you. Let them talk, let them go on babbling. They've been thinking of nothing else for the last month. They've no other thought. Their hearts must have told them of my great love for Calisto, and of all that's gone on between us in the last month. Perhaps they've noticed something, and that's why they're so much more concerned than before about my marriage. But I'm giving them trouble for nothing. It's too late to lock the stable door when the horse has been stolen. No man is going to part me from my joy. No man shall rob me of my pleasures. Calisto is my soul, my life, my lord. All my hopes are in him. I have his word that he will not deceive me. Seeing that he loves me, what other payment could I give him? Every debt in the world is paid in its own way, and love admits only love as payment. To think of him makes me happy, to see him gives me joy, I glory in hearing his voice. Let him do with me what he will, and dispose of me according to his pleasure. Should he decide to cross the sea, I will go with him; to go round the world, I will go too; to sell me in the enemies' country, I shan't refuse his wish. My parents must allow me to enjoy him if they want to enjoy me. They must give up these foolish thoughts about my marriage, for it's better to be a good mistress than a bad wife. They must let me enjoy my youth if they want to enjoy a peaceful old age. Otherwise they'll quickly destroy me and hurry themselves into the grave. All I regret is the time I wasted before I enjoyed him, before I knew him, all those years since I came to know myself. I don't want a husband. I don't want to sully the bonds of matrimony, or tread the steps of marriage with another man, as I find many have done in the old books I've read – women more discreet than I and of higher lineage and estate. Some of them, like Venus, the mother of Aeneas and the love-god Cupid, were worshipped by the heathens as goddesses. Venus was married, but she broke her marriage vow. And others who suffered more violent passions committed wicked and incestuous crimes: Mirra with her father, Semiramis with her son, Canace with her brother, and king David's daughter Thamar, who was raped by her brother. Others did even greater violence to nature's laws, Pasiphae, the wife of king Minos, for instance, with a bull. But they were queens and great ladies, beside whose faults mine will seem mild and venial. For I had good cause to love. I was wooed and requested, I was captivated by his virtues, solicited by that cunning mistress of her art Celestina, who paid me several dangerous visits before I entirely yielded to his love. And now for the last month, as you have seen, not a night has passed in which he hasn't scaled our garden wall like a fort; and many times he has come in vain, but hasn't once shown anger or resentment. His servants were killed on my account, and his fortune is wasting away. He has pretended to everyone that he has left the city and stayed shut up in his house all day waiting to see me at night. So how can I show ingratitude, how can I flatter and betray so true a lover? I want no husband, I want no father or relations. If I lose Calisto I shall have lost my life, which only delights me because I delight him.

LUCRECIA: Be quiet, madam, and listen. They're still talking.

PLEBERIO: Well, what's your opinion, Alisa? Shall we speak to our daughter? Shall we tell her what suitors are asking for her hand, so that she may decide for herself and tell us which of them pleases her? For though they're under paternal authority, the law gives men and girls the right to choose.

ALISA: What do you mean? You'd be wasting your time. If we were to put such an idea to our Melibea she'd be frightened to death. What do you think she knows about men? Or about marriage, or what marriage is, or that men and women come together to make children? How can an innocent virgin possibly feel desire for something she doesn't know and has never heard about? Do you imagine that she can sin, even in imagination? If we command her to take a man, Pleberio, she will certainly obey, whether he's of high birth or low, handsome or ugly. She'll take him gladly, and consider him a good choice. I know my own daughter, for I've watched her and brought her up.

MELIBEA: Lucrecia, Lucrecia, go quickly into the hall. Go through the little door and interrupt them at once. Give them some pretended message to make them stop praising me, or I shall burst out screaming like a madwoman. All their stupid talk about my innocence is more than I can bear.

Act Seventeen

Lacking Penelope's chastity, Elicia decides to stop grieving and mourning for her dead friends. She accepts Areusa's advice and moves to her house, where Sosia visits her. By flattering him, she makes him reveal the whole secret of Calisto's visits to Melibea.

ELICIA: This mourning's doing me no good. Nobody comes to my house, or even walks down the street. No one wakes me with music, and no lovers serenade me. There are no knife fights or night brawls on my account and, what's worse, not a gift or a coin comes in through my door. It's all my own fault. If I'd taken the advice of Areusa, who loves me and is a true sister to me, when I took her news the other day of this sad business that has reduced me to penury, I shouldn't be alone in this house that everyone loathes to visit. Damned if I'll mourn for the fellow! I don't suppose he'd have mourned for me if I'd died. Areusa was quite right when she said to me: 'Never feel or show more grief for another person's death or misfortune than he would for you.' If I had died, Sempronio would still have taken his pleasures. So why should I be so crazy as to grieve because he has been beheaded? He was so wild and bad-tempered that he might very well have killed me, as he killed that poor old lady whom I looked on as my mother. I shall follow Areusa's advice exactly, since she knows the world better than I do. I shall see a great deal of her and earn myself something to live on. I shall enjoy her company, for she's a gay and amusing talker, and one day with the wise, as they say, is better than a lifetime spent with fools and simpletons. So I'll put away my mourning, cast off sorrow and say good-bye to these tears that have been continually starting to my eyes. Since we cry as soon as we're born, it's not surprising if we find it easier to begin than to stop. But it's only sensible to stop, for tears do harm to the eyes, and fine clothes make plain women look beautiful, old women look young, and young women look like girls. Paint and whitening are like bird-lime for snaring men. Come now, lotions and a mirror, for I've spoilt my eyes! On with my white coif and my embroidered ruff and my party clothes! I must make a wash for my hair, for it's losing its golden sheen. And when that's done I'll count my hens and make my bed, for cleanliness gladdens the heart. Then I'll sweep the doorway and sprinkle the pavement to show passers-by that sorrow's banished now. But first I'll go and visit my cousin, and ask her if Sosia has been to see her and what passed between them. I haven't seen her since I told him she wanted to talk to him. I hope to goodness I find her alone. Her house is generally as full of suitors as an inn is of boozers. The door's shut. I don't think she can have a man with her. (*She knocks.*)

AREUSA: Who's that?

ELICIA: It's Elicia. Open the door, darling.

AREUSA: Come in, sister. Gracious me, I am pleased to see you dressed like this, and not in mourning. We'll have good times together now, and I'll come and see you. Sometimes we'll meet in my house and sometimes in yours. Perhaps Celestina's death was a good thing for us both. I feel that life has improved for me already. It's true, as they say, that the dead open the eyes of the living. To some they leave riches, and others, like you, they set free.

ELICIA: Someone's knocking at your door. They don't give us much time to talk. I wanted to ask you if Sosia has been here.

AREUSA: No, he hasn't. We'll talk later. What a banging! I'll go and open the door. It must be a madman, or else a close friend. Who's that knocking?

SOSIA: Let me in, lady. I'm Sosia, Calisto's servant.

AREUSA: Good heavens! Talk of the devil . . . Hide yourself, darling, behind this screen, and just you see how I'll flatter him. By the time he leaves I'll make him think that he's the only man in the world for me. I'll wheedle all his secrets out of him and his master's too, as easily as he combs the dust out of a horse's hide.

Is it Sosia? Is it my secret friend, whom I love dearly though he doesn't know it? The man I've longed to meet because everyone speaks so well of him? So faithful to your master, such a good friend to your comrades! I must embrace you, my love, because now that I see you I believe there are more virtues in you than anyone told me of. Come in. Let's go and sit down. How glad I am to see you! Your face reminds me of that poor fellow Parmeno. The whole day's brighter for bringing you to visit me. Tell me, sir, did you know of me before you came?

SOSIA: You have such a name in the city for charm and wit that you can't be surprised if many people whom you don't know know you. For if anyone talks in praise of pretty women he mentions your name first of all.

ELICIA (*aside*): Well, the poor son of a whore, what fine manners he puts on! Who'd have thought, seeing him ride bareback to water the horses, with his naked legs dangling beneath his smock, that he could strut it now in doublet and hose, and sprout wings and a tongue!

AREUSA: I should be shamed by what you say if anyone were present to hear you make such fun of me. But as all you men carry flatteries on your tongues, and hand your deceitful and ready-made praise out to everybody, I won't let you fluster me. But you've no heed of these blandishments, I assure you, Sosia. I love you without your praising me.

You've won me. You've no need to woo. There were two reasons why I asked you to come and see me. But if you flatter me or lie to me any more I'll tell you neither, though both are to your advantage.

SOSIA: God forbid that I should deceive you, madam. I came here trusting in the great favour that you were to do me, and that you are doing me. I felt unworthy to take off your shoes. Guide my tongue. Answer your own questions for me, and I'll confirm whatever you say.

AREUSA: My love, you know how fond I was of Parmeno, and the proverb, He that loves Bertrand loves all that he has. I liked all his friends, and faithful service done to his master pleased me as much as it pleased him. When he saw harm coming to Calisto he sprang to his defence. Such being the case, I wanted firstly that you should know the love I feel for you and how pleased I shall always be to receive your visits. You won't lose by them if I can help it. On the contrary you'll gain. And secondly, ever since I first saw you and loved you I've wanted to warn you to look after yourself and especially to tell your secrets to nobody. For you saw what trouble came to Parmeno and Sempronio because they confided in Celestina. I shouldn't like you to meet the same wretched death. I've wept quite enough tears already. I must tell you, however, that a certain person came to me and said that you had told him all about the love of Calisto and Melibea – how he won her, and how you went out every night as his bodyguard, and many other things that I shouldn't care to repeat. Remember, my friend, that only women give away secrets, and not all women either but ordinary women and girls. Be careful, or you may get into great trouble. Remember God gave you two eyes and two ears and only one tongue, so that you should see and hear twice as much as you say. Remember that you can never be certain your friend will keep the secret you tell him, since you're not able to keep it yourself. When you have to accompany your master to that lady's house you should never make a noise. Don't let the earth hear your footsteps. But I've been told that you go there every night bawling like a crazy roisterer.

SOSIA: If that's the story they told you, they're a long way from the truth. In fact, they don't know what they're talking about. Anyone who says he heard any secret from my lips is telling a lie. Some people may have seen me going out on moonlit nights to water my horses, laughing and singing and joking to banish cares and keep my spirits up. But as that was before ten o'clock, they've jumped to false conclusions, taken their conclusions for facts, and are now swearing to the truth of their own fancies. Calisto would have been mad to go out at such an hour on such important business. He waits till everyone is in bed, enjoying the sweetness of early slumber, and he doesn't go every night, for such affairs don't allow of nightly visits. But if you want further proof that they're lying, for they say it's easier to catch a liar than a lame man, we haven't been there more than eight times in a month, and yet these busybodies say we've been every night.

AREUSA: Now, if you love me, dear friend, tell me which days you decide to go, so that I can confront them and catch them out in their own lies. If they give the wrong day I shall be sure that you're keeping your secret and that they are merely slanderers. And if their statement is untrue, you will not be running into danger and I shan't be alarmed for your life. For I hope to enjoy your company for a long time.

SOSIA: Let's put it to the proof immediately, madam. He's arranged to visit her by way of the garden tonight as the clock strikes twelve. Ask them tomorrow what they know, and if anyone gives you the true facts, may I be shorn like a criminal.

AREUSA: But tell me which way you'll go, my love, so that I can contradict them better if I find they tell me wrong.

SOSIA: Past the fat friar's, along the path behind his house.

ELICIA (*aside*): That's got you, you poor beggar! It's all that we need. God help anyone who trusts himself to that miserable mule-driver! He'll blab all the secrets he knows.

AREUSA: Brother Sosia, you've given me enough evidence to prove your innocence and the wickedness of your enemies. Now good-bye. I've some other business to do, and I've spent a long time with you.

ELICIA (*aside*): Clever woman! That's the right leave-taking, and just what the ass deserves for giving up his secret so easily.

SOSIA: Sweet and gracious lady, forgive me if I've wearied you by staying so long. Whenever you care to call on me you will find no one so ready to risk his life in your service. May angels guard you!

AREUSA: God be with you.... Out you go, mule-driver. You look very pleased with yourself, I'll be bound. But I've tricked you, you rogue, and pardon me if I turn my back. Come out, sister. What do you think of the way I dismissed him? A fine fellow you are! I know how to deal with his sort. That's the right treatment for asses. I cudgel them as I did that one. If they're wild I curb them; if they're bashful I scare them; if they're pious I fluster them; and if they're chaste I excite them. I'll tell you this, cousin, mine's a different art from Celestina's. She took me for a fool because I was content that she should. Now that we know all we want to about this matter, we must go to the house of that other fellow with the hangdog look whom I dismissed so rudely when you were here last Thursday. You must pretend that you want to reconcile us, and have asked me to come and see him.

Act Eighteen

Elicia resolves to take Areusa's advice and make peace between her and Centurio. They go to Centurio's house, and request him to revenge the three deaths on Calisto and Melibea. He promises to do so, but true to his ruffian's nature breaks his word, as will presently appear.

ELICIA: Is there anyone at home?

CENTURIO: Run, boy, and see who has dared to enter without knocking. No, come back, come back. I see who it is. Don't muffle yourself in your cloak, madam. You can't hide from me. Once I saw Elicia come in I guessed she wasn't bringing bad company or displeasing news. I knew she was bringing me pleasure.

AREUSA: Let's turn back, for heaven's sake. The rogue's getting proud. He thinks I've come to make up to him. But he'd rather have a visit from women of his own kind than from us. Let's go out, please. His ugly face makes me feel sick. Do you think you've brought me for a pleasant walk, sister, or that it's right to come and see this villainous creature directly after vespers?

ELICIA: Come back, if you love me. Don't go away. You'll leave half your cloak in my hands if you do.

CENTURIO: Hold her, I beg of you, madam. Hold her. Don't let her get away.

ELICIA: I wonder if you're in your right mind, sister? A man may be wild and crazy, but surely he'll be pleased to receive a visit, especially from ladies? Come here, Centurio. I'm determined she shall embrace you. If I have to use force I'll take the blame for it.

AREUSA: I'd rather see him arrested and put to death by his

enemies than give him that pleasure. No, no! I've done with him for the rest of my life. What do I owe this foul man that I should embrace him or ever set eyes on him again? Why only the other day I asked him to go a very short distance and do me a service on which my life depended, and he refused.

CENTURIO: Ask me to do anything I can, madam, anything in my own trade. Ask me to challenge three men together and if more come I swear I won't run away. Ask me to kill a man or cut off a leg or an arm or slash any woman's face that has entered into competition with you. Anything like that I'll do on request. But don't ask me to go a journey or give you money. Money doesn't stay with me. I could turn three somersaults and not a farthing would drop out of my pockets. Nobody can give what he hasn't got. In this house of mine, as you see, a fool could walk anywhere without tripping over anything. I've no more possessions than a soldier on the frontier: a jar with a broken brim and a blunted spit. The bed on which I lie is bound with the hoops of bucklers. A pile of broken mail is my mattress, and a dice-box my pillow. If I wanted to give an entertainment I have nothing left to pawn except this torn cloak that I'm wearing.

ELICIA: Bless my soul, but I like the way he talks! He's as humble as a saint, he speaks to you like an angel, and he talks good sense. What more do you want of him? Speak to him, for goodness sake, and stop being angry, for he's putting himself willingly at your service.

CENTURIO: At her service d'you say, madam? I swear by all the blessed martyrs from A to Z that my arm quivers at the thought of all I shall do for her. I'm always thinking how to please her, and never succeed. Last night I dreamt that I was fighting four men – she knows who they are – whom I'd challenged on her behalf, and that I killed one of them. And of those that ran away, the one who escaped most lightly left his left arm at my feet. But I'd do much more for her by day, when I'm awake, if anyone so much as touched her shoe.

AREUSA: I'll take you up on that. We've come at the right moment. I'll forgive you on condition that you take vengeance for me on a gentleman called Calisto, who has annoyed my cousin and me.

CENTURIO: Damn the conditions! Tell me immediately, has the man made confession?

AREUSA: You needn't bother about his soul.

CENTURIO: Very well. Let's send him to dine in hell unconfessed.

AREUSA: Listen and don't interrupt me. You'll catch him tonight.

CENTURIO: Say no more. I understand. I know all about his love and the two men who died for him. I know how this concerns you ladies, and I know which way he goes and at what time and to whom. But tell me how many men escort him?

AREUSA: Two lads.

CENTURIO: A small job. Not much work for my sword, I'm afraid. There's more for it to do somewhere else tonight where I've promised to go.

AREUSA: That's just an excuse. Don't tell me that story. I won't be put off till tomorrow. I want to know whether deeds and words are the same thing with you.

CENTURIO: If my sword told all it did, it wouldn't have time to finish the tale. What else but my sword fills the graveyards? What else makes the surgeons' fortunes in these parts? What else keeps the armourers so busy? What else destroys fine mail? What else shivers Barcelona bucklers? What else slices Calatayud helmets? It carves Almazan casques like ripe melons. I've earned my living by it for twenty years. It's made the men fear me and the women love me, except you. It earned my grandfather the name of Centurio, and my father too, and me after him.

ELICIA: What did your sword do to earn your grandfather that name? Tell me, did it make him captain of a hundred men?

CENTURIO: No, it made him pimp of a hundred women.

AREUSA: Let's not talk of lineage and ancient deeds. If you're going to do what I ask, decide and don't put it off, because we want to go now.

CENTURIO: How I long for night to fall! I'm more eager to oblige you than you are to be avenged. But so that I may please you entirely, choose the death you want me to give him. I can show you here and now a repertory containing seven hundred and seventy kinds of death. You'll see which one you prefer.

ELICIA: For heaven's sake, Areusa, don't entrust the deed to this wild fellow. Better leave it undone than scandalize the city. That will bring us more harm than we've suffered already.

AREUSA: Quiet, sister! Tell us a death that doesn't make much noise.

CENTURIO: Those that I use most in these days, and am handiest at, are a sound beating with a sheathed sword, which draws no blood, or a thrashing with the pommel, or a quick stab in the back. Some I pierce with fine holes like a sieve, others I carve deep, or slash all over, or kill at a thrust. Some I thrash with a club, to give my sword a rest.

ELICIA: Don't go on, for God's sake. Give him a thrashing that will punish him, but don't kill him.

CENTURIO: I swear by Christ's body in the litany that my arm's no more capable of giving a thrashing that doesn't kill than the sun is of ceasing to move through the sky.

AREUSA: Let's not be soft-hearted, sister. Let him do as he likes and kill him as he fancies. Melibea shall weep as you have done. Let's leave it to him. Take good care to do what I asked, Centurio. Whichever way you do it we shall be pleased. But be sure he doesn't escape some punishment for his crime.

CENTURIO: May God forgive him! He won't escape me unless he takes to his heels. I'm very grateful, madam, that a chance has occurred, even though a small one, for me to show you what I will do for love of you.

AREUSA: May God guide your right hand! I commend you to him. And now we must go.

CENTURIO: God be with you too and make you more patient with your friends.... Well, there go those two stubborn whores, and good riddance! Now I must consider how I'm to get out of my promise, but in such a way that they'll think I've tried my very hardest to keep it. I don't want them to imagine I've neglected it for fear of running into danger. I might pretend to be ill, but what good would that be? They would repeat their request when I recovered. If I were to say that I went there and put them all to flight, they would want proof of who they were, and how many, and where I found them, and how they were dressed, and I shouldn't know the answers. I'm in an awkward position! How am I to satisfy them without risk to myself? I will send for that lame fellow Traso and his mates, and say that as I'm busy tonight on another matter they must go and raise a disturbance for me. I'll tell them just to clatter their shields as if they were fighting, so as to give certain young men a good fright. I'll say I undertook the job and can't do it, and that it's safe enough and can't lead to trouble. All they've got to do is frighten these young men away and then go home to bed.

Act Nineteen

Calisto goes with Sosia and Tristan to Melibea's garden, where she is waiting for him with Lucrecia. On the way, Sosia tells his master of his conversation with Areusa. When Calisto is in the garden with Melibea, Traso and others come, on Centurio's instructions, to fulfil his promise to Areusa and Elicia. Sosia goes to meet them, and Calisto, hearing the noise in the street, rushes to the ladder, which brings him to his death – the usual reward of such lovers and a warning to others to avoid such intrigues.

SOSIA: Quietly, quietly, or someone may hear us. But on our way to Pleberio's garden, I'll tell you, friend Tristan, about a conversation I had with Areusa today, which makes me the happiest man in the world. It seems that she'd heard such good things of me that she fell in love with me, and so she sent for me to pay her a visit. She gave me some very sensible advice, which I won't bother to mention, and showed me quite plainly that she was as much my woman now as ever she was Parmeno's. She asked me to come and see her regularly, and said that she hoped to enjoy my love for a long time. But I swear to you, brother, by the dangerous road we're walking and by my blessed life, that I was two or three times tempted to take her on the spot. I was too bashful, however. She was so beautiful and so well-dressed, and I was wearing my old moth-eaten cloak. Each time she moved she gave off an odour of musk; and I smelt of the horse dung that was sticking to my boots. Her hands were white as snow; each time she took off her glove, it was as if she were scattering orange blossom through the house. For that reason, and because she had some business to do, I postponed my assault for another day. Besides, not everything can be managed at a first visit. After a few conversations one comes to a better understanding.

TRISTAN: It'd take someone older and more experienced than I to give you proper advice about this business, brother Sosia. But for what youth and average intelligence are worth, I'll say this: By your own admission, the woman is a well-known whore; and you can be sure there's some catch in this conversation you had with her. Her protestations were not genuine, but I don't know what she hoped to gain by them. If she loves you for your fine manners, she's rejected plenty with finer; if it's for your wealth, she knows that all you've got is the dust that clings to you from the curry-comb; if it's for your high descent, she knows perfectly well that your name's Sosia and so was your father's, that you were born and bred in a village, and broke the clods with a plough, in fact that you're better equipped as a ploughman than a lover. Take care, Sosia, and consider whether she wasn't trying to learn something from you about this errand we're on at present. Perhaps she envies Melibea her pleasure, and wants to make trouble between Calisto and Pleberio. Remember that once envy's taken root it's an incurable disease and a tiresome guest to entertain, for it never yields any reward and enjoys other people's disasters. If I'm right about this, she's trying to deceive you with this show of grandeur that they all know how to put on, and she's so poisonously jealous that she's willing to damn her soul if she can accomplish her designs. In fact, she'll set everyone at odds to get her own confounded way. She may offer you white bread, the wicked creature, but she'll spread rat-poison on it. And if she can make trouble she'll sell you her body to do it. Take my advice and spring a trap on her, and I'll tell you how. For cheat a cheat . . . but you understand me. The vixen may be clever, but the hunter's cleverer.

Well, meet her plots with a plot of your own, and scale the fortress when she thinks she's safe. Then once back in your stable you can sing to yourself, The bay mare thinks one thing but the man who rides her another.

SOSIA: What a clever lad you are, Tristan! You've said more than I'd expect from one so young, and raised a shrewd suspicion in me. I think you're right. But we're coming to the garden and our master is on our heels. So we'll leave this conversation for another day. There's still a lot to say.

CALISTO: Set up the ladder, lads, and keep quiet. I think I can hear my mistress talking inside. I'll climb to the top of the wall and listen from there. Perhaps I shall hear something that will tell me how much she loves me when I'm away.

MELIBEA: Go on singing, Lucrecia, till my lord comes. I enjoy listening to you. Sing softly and keep beneath the trees in case anyone passing should hear us.

LUCRECIA:

If I owned this garden
  And all its bounteous flowers
I would pluck your kisses
  In the morning hours.

The lilies and the roses
  Would make their colours new.
They would revive their odours
  Each day as I walked through.

MELIBEA: Oh how sweet it is to hear you! It makes me melt with delight. Go on, if you love me.

LUCRECIA:

Welcome is the fountain
  To one whose throat is dry
But pleasanter Calisto's face
  To Melibea's eye.

For though the night be dark
  She will enjoy the sight
Of her love leaping o'er the wall
  And kiss him with delight.
The wolf leaps with pleasure
  When he sees the lambs;
The little goats leap to the teat,
  And she leaps to his arms.
Never did lady welcome
  Her love with more delight
Never did garden witness love
  More tireless any night.

MELIBEA: When you sing, Lucrecia, I seem to see him here before my very eyes. Go on, for you are in very good voice, and I'll sing an accompaniment.

MELIBEA and LUCRECIA:

Sweet trees, throw down your shade
  And bow when you descry
The sweet eyes that you long for,
  The sweet steps drawing nigh!
And O you stars, shine out,
  Pole-star and star of day!
Why find you not my sleeping joy
  And rouse him with your ray?

MELIBEA: Listen to me now, please. I'm going to sing alone.

Parrots and nightingales
  O sing to greet the light,
Carry a message to my love
  That I await his sight,
The midnight hour has struck
  And still he does not come.
Ask if he has another love
  Who keeps him in her room.

CALISTO: The sweetness of your singing overwhelms me. I cannot bear to wait any longer in painful expectation, my dear lady, sole joy of my heart! Was ever woman born who could rival your charms? But how swiftly you broke off your delightful song! Could my poor heart not bear to wait? Why did I interrupt your joy to accomplish our joint desires?

MELIBEA: A pleasing wrong! A sweet surprise! Can it be my lord and soul? Is it he? I can't believe it. Where have you been hiding, my bright sun? Where did you keep your face hidden? Had you been listening long? Why did you let me breathe senseless words on the air with my harsh swan's voice? The whole garden rejoices that you have come. Look at the moon, how clearly she has shown her face! Look at the clouds scudding by. Listen to the water flowing from this little spring. How much softer it sounds, and how much more liquid in the fresh grass! Listen to the tall cypresses, how peacefully their branches kiss, driven to it by a little warm breeze that sways them. Look at their quiet shadows. How dark they are and ready to conceal our joys! What is the matter, Lucrecia? Have you gone mad with pleasure? Let him alone. Don't tear him to pieces. Don't burden his body with your heavy embraces. Let me enjoy what is mine. Don't disturb my pleasure.

CALISTO: Glorious lady, don't interrupt your sweet song if you wish me to live. Don't let my delightful presence be less agreeable to you than my grievous absence.

MELIBEA: How can you ask me to sing, my love? How can I sing when it was my longing for you that governed my voice and produced the song? Now that you've come at last, my longing has vanished and I can sing no longer. And you, sir, who are the pattern of courtesy and good breeding, how can you ask me to sing if you cannot control your restless hands? Why can't you give up these tricks? Why can't you command your hands to be still and stop this horrid practice, these unbearable familiarities? Gently, angel, for just as I love to have you quietly beside me, so I hate this rough treatment. When you act decorously I'm pleased, but your rude hands rasp me when they get rough. Don't disturb my clothes. If you want to know whether I'm wearing silk or wool, why do you fumble with my shift? It's linen, I can tell you. We can sport and play in a thousand other ways that I'll show you, but don't hurt and ill-treat me as you do. What advantage do you get from destroying my clothes?

CALISTO: He who wants to eat the bird, plucks its feathers first.

LUCRECIA: I'm damned if I'll listen any more. What a life! Here am I with my heart melting and she playing at shyness to egg him on. Good, good, they've stopped arguing. They needed no peace-makers. I could do just as well myself, if those fools of servants would come and ask me some time. But they expect me to go and entreat them.

MELIBEA: My lord, would you like me to ask Lucrecia to bring us some refreshment?

CALISTO: The only refreshment for me is to have your lovely body in my power. You can get food and drink anywhere if you pay for it, and you can get it at any time, and anyone can get it. But how can you expect me to abandon for even one moment what can't be bought, and exists nowhere on earth but in this garden, and has no equal anywhere?

LUCRECIA: My head aches from listening, but they never tire of talking, nor their arms of embracing, nor their lips of kissing. Good! They're quiet at last. Third time lucky, it seems.

CALISTO: I wish the dawn would never break. My senses get

such joy and comfort from the noble contemplation of your soft limbs.

MELIBEA: My lord, it is I who get delight. I am the gainer. Your attentions are infinitely gratifying to me.

SOSIA: Get out, you rogues! Don't try and frighten me. I'm not afraid of you. Just wait till I get at you, and I'll send you rascals packing as you deserve.

CALISTO: That's Sosia shouting, lady. Let me go and see that they don't kill him. He's only got one young page with him. Quickly, give me my cloak. It's underneath you.

MELIBEA: Oh, what an unlucky chance! Don't go without your cuirass. Come back and put it on.

CALISTO: What a sword and a cloak and a good heart can't do, lady, a cuirass and a casque and cowardice won't.

SOSIA: So, you've come again? Stay a moment, and I'll make you sorry ...

CALISTO: Let me go, lady, if you please. The ladder's in position.

MELIBEA: Alas for Melibea! How can you go so rudely and in such haste without your cuirass, to face you know not what? Lucrecia, come here quickly. Calisto has gone. He heard a noise. Let's throw his cuirass over the wall. It's lying here.

TRISTAN: Mind, sir! Don't come down. They've gone away. It was only that lame fellow Traso and some other rogues shouting as they went past. Sosia is coming back now. Be careful, sir, hold on to the ladder.

CALISTO: O Blessed Virgin preserve me! I'm dying. A confessor!

TRISTAN: Come here quickly, Sosia. Our poor master has fallen off the ladder. He's not speaking. He's not moving.

SOSIA: Sir, sir! Try the other ear! ... He's dead, stone dead! Alas, alas!

LUCRECIA: Listen, listen! Something dreadful has happened.

MELIBEA: O poor wretch that I am, what's this I hear?

TRISTAN: Dead, my good master dead! My master fell off the wall. A sad death without confession. Gather our poor master's brains from the stones, Sosia, and put them back in his skull. An unlucky day, and alas, a sudden end!

MELIBEA: Oh, alas, alas! What's this I hear? What terrible thing can have happened? Help me climb up the wall, Lucrecia, and I'll see what it is. If you don't I'll rouse my father's house with shouting. My love and joy, all has passed like smoke! Gone is my happiness. My glory is over.

LUCRECIA: Tristan, my love, what's the matter? Why are you weeping so bitterly?

TRISTAN: I'm weeping for my sorrow, I'm weeping for my great grief. My master Calisto has fallen from the ladder and is dead. His head is split in pieces. He died unconfessed. Tell his sad new mistress never to expect her unfortunate lover again. Take his feet, Sosia. Let us carry our dear master's body away, so that he shan't suffer dishonour because he died in this place. And let us weep as we go. In grief and solitude and desolation let us clothe ourselves in mourning, let us put on sad sackcloth.

MELIBEA: O bitterest of all sorrows! How fleeting was joy, how quickly grief followed!

LUCRECIA: Do not scratch your face or tear your hair, lady. Joy today, tomorrow sadness. What planet can it have been that so speedily changed its aspect? But show more courage. Get up, for God's sake, and don't let your father find you in this suspicious place. They'll hear you if you go on like this. Madam, madam, can't you hear me? Don't swoon, for heaven's sake! Take courage to bear your grief, since you were bold enough to take your pleasures.

MELIBEA: Do you hear what those lads are saying? Can you

hear how sadly they sing? Do you hear their prayers and responses as they bear away all my joy, all my happiness dead? Shall I enjoy my heart's delight no more? For how short a while I held my glory, and now it has slipped from my hands. How ungrateful we mortals are, never recognizing our good fortune until we have lost it!

LUCRECIA: Come to your senses, come to your senses! You'll bring more trouble on yourself if they find you in the garden than you found pleasure in Calisto's visits, or grief when you saw him dead. Let's go back to your room and put you to bed. I'll call your father, and we'll pretend you are ill again, for there's no chance of concealment now.

Act Twenty

Lucrecia knocks at Pleberio's door and, when he asks her what she wants, begs him to go quickly and see his daughter. He consoles her and asks what is wrong. Melibea pretends to have a pain in her heart and sends her father to fetch musical instruments. She and Lucrecia climb up a tower. She sends Lucrecia away and shuts the door. Her father comes to the foot of the tower, and she tells him the whole story of what has happened. Then she throws herself down.

PLEBERIO: What do you want, Lucrecia? Why are you in such a hurry? Why are you so wild and distressed? What is the matter with my daughter? Has she suddenly been taken ill, that you can't give me time to put on my clothes or even get out of bed?

LUCRECIA: Sir, be very quick if you want to see her alive. She's been taken violently ill. She's so changed that I can scarcely recognize her.

PLEBERIO: Come quickly then. Go on. You must enter first. Lift the hangings and open that window wide so that I can get a clear look at her face. What is the matter, girl? Are you in pain? Where is the pain? What has happened to you? Why have you become so weak? Look at me, it's your father. Speak to me, for heaven's sake, tell me the cause of your trouble, and it shall quickly be cured. Don't send my grey hairs in sorrow to the grave. You know you're my only treasure. Open those sweet eyes and look at me.

MELIBEA: Oh, how I suffer!

PLEBERIO: No suffering could be as bad as seeing you suffer. Your mother fainted as soon as she heard you were ill. She is so upset she could not come to see you. Pull yourself together, take courage and summon the strength to come with me and see her. Tell me, dear soul, what caused your grief?

MELIBEA: The cure is lost. There's no cure now.

PLEBERIO: Beloved daughter, your old father's darling, don't let the cruel anguish of this illness drive you to despair. Only weak hearts are overcome by pain. If you'll tell me your trouble, it shall quickly be cured. We don't lack medicines or doctors or servants to bring you back to health, or herbs, or stones or spells or the secret virtue that's found in the bodies of animals, if those are what we need. But don't torture me any more, don't destroy me, or drive me out of my mind, but tell me what's the matter.

MELIBEA: A mortal wound, right through the heart, which will not let me speak. It isn't like other diseases. To cure it you must pluck my heart out, for it's wounded right inside.

PLEBERIO: Too soon you've caught the grief of old age. Youth should be all joy and happiness, and the enemy of sorrow. Get up, and let's go and breathe the fresh air of the river. When you are with your mother, you'll recover your spirits and your pain will pass. Come, don't refuse comfort. It'll be the best remedy for your sickness.

MELIBEA: Let's go as you say. We'll climb on to the roof, from there we can enjoy a fine view of the ships, and perhaps that will somewhat ease my grief.

PLEBERIO: We'll go up then, and take Lucrecia with us.

MELIBEA: But I pray you, Father, have some stringed instrument brought to me so that I can wile away my grief by singing and playing. For though my sufferings torment me, sweet sounds and harmonies will much abate it.

PLEBERIO: I'll do so immediately, daughter. I'll go and see to it.

MELIBEA: Lucrecia, my friend, this place is too high, and I miss my father. Go and ask him to stand at the foot of the tower, because I want to tell him something that I forgot, something he must say to my mother.

LUCRECIA: I'll go, Madam.

MELIBEA: Everyone has left me, and I've now contrived a way of dying. It gives me some consolation to know that soon we shall be together, I and my dear lover Calisto. I will shut the door, so that no one may come up to prevent my death. They shan't prevent my going. No one shall stop the way by which very soon I shall be able to visit him today who visited me last night. Everything has conformed to my plan, and I shall have time to tell my lord Pleberio the cause of my premature end. I am greatly wronging his grey hairs, bringing much grief to his old age. Many sorrows will fall on him because of my sin. I leave him in great desolation. But even if my death should shorten my parents' days, others have certainly been crueller to theirs. Prusias, king of Bithynia killed his father, for no reason, having no grievance against him; Ptolemy king of Egypt killed his father, his mother, his brothers, and his wife in order to enjoy a mistress; and Orestes murdered his mother Clytemnestra; the cruel Emperor Nero had his mother Agrippina killed just for the joy he took in murder. They are wicked, they are the true parricides, but I am not. If I give pain by my death, at least I am expiating the crime of causing them grief. Others have been far more cruel, and killed sons and brothers. Beside their crimes mine will appear slight. Philip, king of Macedon; Herod, king of Judah; Constantine, emperor of Rome; Laodice, queen of Cappadocia, and the witch Medea: all of them killed their dear children and lovers for no reason and preserved their own lives. Finally I remember the great cruelty of Phrates, king of the Parthians, who killed his old father Orodos, his only son, and thirty brothers and sisters in order to leave no heir. These crimes were wicked indeed, for they killed their elders, descendants, and brothers, while remaining safe themselves. It is true that even so we should not imitate their evil-doing. But it is now out of my hands. You, Lord, who have been witness to what I've said, you see how little is my strength, how my liberty is lost, how my feelings have been captured by love for that gentleman who is dead, a love so powerful that it destroys the love I have for my living parents.

PLEBERIO: What are you doing up there, Melibea? Why are you alone? What do you want to say to me? Would you like me to come up?

MELIBEA: Don't attempt to come up here, Father, or you'll interrupt what I want to say to you. Soon you'll be weeping for the death of your only daughter. I have come to my end. I am drawing near to my rest and you to your sorrow, I to my comfort and you to your grief. Now is the time when I shall have company and you will be alone. There'll be no need of instruments to soothe my sorrow, only of bells for the burial of my body. If you can listen without weeping you'll hear the desperate cause of my forced but happy departure. Do not interrupt me with words or tears, or you'll suffer more by not knowing why I have died than by seeing me dead. Ask me no questions, and do not demand to know more than I wish to tell you. For when the heart is heavy with grief, the ears are closed to counsel, and at such times good advice rather inflames than allays the passions. Listen, dear Father, to my last words, and if you receive them as I hope, you will not blame my fault. You can see and hear the mourning that afflicts the whole city. You can hear the tolling of bells, the shouting of the people, the barking of dogs and the clash of arms. I was the cause of all this. I have today clothed in sackcloth and mourning the majority of the city's gentlemen, I have left many servants masterless, I have robbed many poor and destitute people of alms and relief, I have been the occasion for sending the most accomplished man ever endowed with graces to keep company with the dead. I have sent out of the land of the living the pattern of nobility and gallantry, of charm and adornment, of speech, carriage, courtesy, and virtue. Thanks to me earth enjoys before her time the noblest body and freshest youth ever born into the world in our days. Though it will astonish you to hear of my strange sin, I will tell you more fully what happened.

Many days ago, Father, a knight named Calisto, whom you knew well, was grieving for love of me. You knew his parents also, and his noble descent; he was famous for his virtues and his courtesy to everyone. He was so tortured by his love and had so little opportunity of speaking to me that he disclosed his passion to a wise and cunning old woman called Celestina, whom he sent to visit me and who dragged the secret of my love from my heart. I told her what I had concealed from my beloved mother. She found a way of winning me to her will, and brought his desires and mine to fruition. He loved me greatly and he was not disappointed. She contrived the sweet and ill-fated consummation of his desires. Subdued by love for him I let him into your house. He scaled the walls of your garden with a ladder, and overcame my resistance. I lost my virginity, and we enjoyed the sinful pleasures of our love for almost a month. Last night he came in the usual way, and just as he was about to return home, Fortune, in her mutability, disposing of all things in her disorderly way, put an end to our joy. The walls were high, the night was dark, the ladder was weak, and the servants he brought with him unused to this kind of service. He was descending in a hurry, having heard a noise in the road where his servants were waiting, and in his confusion failed to see the rungs, put a foot out into the void and fell. Alas, he fell on his head and scattered his brains over the stones and the wall. The Fates cut short his life. They cut him off unconfessed and with him all my hopes, my joy and delight in his company. How cruel it would be, Father, after his death from that fall, that I should live on in grief! His death calls for mine. It invites me, it compels me to be swift and allows no delay. It summons me to fall also, so that I may follow him in everything. It shall not be said of me that dead and gone is soon forgotten. I shall content him in my death, since I had not time to do so in my life. O my loved lord Calisto! Wait for me, I am coming. Wait if you expect me, and don't blame me for staying to give this last account to my father, for I owe him this and much more. Beloved father, I beg you if you loved me in my painful life that is now over, that we may be buried together and our funerals be celebrated together also. Before my welcome release I would say some words of consolation to you that I have chosen and gathered from those ancient books that you made me read for the improvement of my mind. But alas, my memory is confused by the tumult of my grief, and by the sight of your ill-restrained tears trickling down your wrinkled cheeks, and so I have forgotten them. Carry my farewell to my dear mother, and tell her carefully the sad reasons for my death. I am glad not to see her here. Accept, dear father, the penalties of old age; for in a long life sorrows must be endured. Receive this tribute to your years, and receive your beloved daughter in your arms. I grieve for myself, I grieve for you, and much more for my old mother. God be with you and her. To him I offer my soul, and to you for burial my body, that is now coming down to you.

Act Twenty-One

Pleberio returns to his room weeping bitterly, and Alisa asks him the cause of his sudden grief. He tells her of their daughter's death, and shows her Melibea's shattered body. The work concludes with his lamentation.

ALISA: What's the matter, Pleberio? Why are you weeping and crying? I have been lying here senseless since I fainted on hearing that our daughter was in pain. But now your shouts and groans have roused me. Your tears and grief and unaccustomed lamentations have struck me to the heart, revived my numbed senses, and dispelled my previous sorrow. One grief, one passion has driven out the other. Tell me what you are bewailing. Why are you cursing your honourable old age? Why are you tearing your white hair? Why do you call on death? Why are you scratching your venerable face? Has something terrible happened to Melibea? In God's name tell me, for if she is suffering I no longer want to live.

PLEBERIO: Oh, oh, noble wife! Our joy is drowned, and all our happiness gone. Our life is worth nothing now. There is no pain like that of sudden grief, one unexpected blow following on another. It will drive you quickly to the tomb. But I cannot weep alone for the sad loss that has struck us both. Here is the daughter you bore and I engendered. Gaze on her shattered body. She told me the cause, but I learnt it more fully from her sorrowful maid. Join me in weeping our latter years that have now come upon us, all of you who come to share my grief. Help me, my friends, to bewail my misery. My daughter who was my sole treasure! It would be cruelty in me to outlive you. My seventy years were riper for the grave than your twenty. The due order of death was reversed by the grief that overwhelmed you. My hair has grown white only from sorrow, and earth should receive it more gladly than the fair locks that lie here. The rest of my days will be too many. I will complain against death for being so slow and leaving me here alone, now that you have gone. What have I left in life now that I have lost your delightful company? Get up from where she lies, Alisa, and if any life is left in you join me in bewailing her, pour it out in groans and sighs and lamentations. But if your spirit has joined hers, if you have already left this life of grief, why have you wished me to suffer everything alone? You women have the advantage over us that a great grief can painlessly remove you from the world, or at least make you swoon and thus give you some ease. What a hard heart has a father, that it does not break with grief at the loss of its one beloved child! For whom did I build towers? For whom did I acquire honours? For whom did I plant trees? For whom construct ships? O hard earth, how can you still support my steps? Where will my disconsolate old age find shelter? O Fortune, you are indeed minister and steward of temporal wealth, how mutable you are! Why did you not turn your cruel wrath on me? Why did you not overwhelm with your changing tides me who am truly your subject? Why did you not destroy my wealth? Why did you not burn my house? Why did you not reduce my great inheritance to dust? You might have left me that flourishing plant, over which you should have had no power. O fickle Fortune, if you had given me an unhappy youth and a glad old age, you would not have perverted nature. I could have borne the cruelty of your deceptions better in my strong and vigorous youth than in my weak and declining age.

O life full of griefs and miseries! O world, world! Many men have said many things of you, many have inveighed against you for your deceits. They have said many things of you by hearsay, but I will speak from the sad experience of one whose sales and purchases at your deceptive fair have not gone well, of one who has long concealed your double-dealing for fear of arousing your wrath by my hatred, and so that you should not prematurely wither this flower that has today fallen into your grasp. But now I am not afraid, for I have nothing more to lose. Now I am weary of your company. I am like a poor traveller who sings loudly on his way since he has nothing to fear from the cruel highwaymen. I believed in my youth that you and your deeds were governed by some order. But now that I have seen the pro and contra of your dealings, I find in you only a maze of error, a frightful desert, a den of wild beasts, a game in which men go round in circles, a lake full of mud, a country choked with thorns, a high mountain, a stony meadow, a field swarming with snakes, an orchard all blossom and no fruit, a fountain of cares, a river of tears, a sea of miseries, labour without profit, sweet poison, vain hope, false joy, and real sorrow. Feed us, false world, with the food of your delights, and in the tastiest morsel we find the hook. We cannot escape it for it has ensnared our wills. You promise much but perform nothing. You throw us from you so that we shall not beg you to keep your empty promises. Carelessly and thoughtlessly we run in the meadows of your rank vices, and you show us the trap when we have no chance of turning back. Many have forsaken you for fear you might suddenly forsake them, and they will count themselves lucky when they see the reward you have given this poor old man in payment for his long services. You put out our eyes and then anoint our brows to comfort us. So that no sad man shall find himself alone in adversity, you hurt everyone. You tell us that it consoles miserable men like myself to have companions in sorrow. But I am alone in my grief, disconsolate and old.

No man's misfortune is like mine. Though I search my weary memory of the present and the past I can find no one who has suffered a similar grief. If I recall the stoical patience of Paulus Emilius, whose two sons were killed within a week yet who bore his loss with such courage that the Roman people took more comfort from him than he from them, I am not consoled, for he had two sons left to him, whom he had adopted. What sort of companion in my grief should I find in the Athenian captain Pericles, or in the valiant Xenophon, since their sons died in foreign lands? It could not have cost Pericles much not to change countenance but to keep a calm expression, or for Xenophon to tell the messenger who brought him the sad news of his son's death that he would receive no penalty because he himself felt no sorrow. There is no resemblance here to my misfortune.

Even less could you say, O world full of evils, that Anaxagoras and I were alike in our grief and loss, and that I could repeat of my beloved daughter what he said of his only son: 'Being mortal, I knew that whatever I engendered must die.' For my Melibea killed herself before my eyes, of her own free will, driven to it by the cruel love that tortured her, whereas his son was killed in righteous battle. There is no loss like mine. A stricken old man, I seek comfort but find nothing to comfort me. The royal prophet David, who wept when his son was sick, refused to weep for him dead since he said it was almost madness to weep for what could not be remedied, and he had many children left to comfort him in his loss. But I am not weeping for her sad death, but for the terrible manner of it. O my unhappy daughter, with you I lose the fears and apprehensions that alarmed me every day. Your death alone has had the power to free me from anxieties.

What shall I do when I go to your room and find it empty? What shall I do when you do not answer my knock? Who could fill the void that you leave in me? No one has lost what I have lost today, not the valiant Lambas of Auria, Duke of Athens, who with his own hands threw his wounded son overboard into the sea. All these were deaths suffered in the cause of honour. But what forced my daughter to slay herself was the mighty power of love. False world, what comfort can you give me in my tired old age? How can you expect me to remain alive, now that I know the tricks and snares, the chains and nets, in which you capture our weak wills? Where have you taken my daughter? Who will be my companion in my companionless home? Who will look after me in my failing years? O love, love, I did not think you had the strength and power to kill your victims. You wounded me in my youth, but I survived your fires. Why did you let me go, only to pay me out for my escape in my old age? I thought myself free from your snares when I came to the age of forty and was happy in my wife's company and in the fruit of our union that you have plucked today. I did not think you would visit your spite against the fathers upon the children, or know that you could wound with the sword and burn with fire. You leave the clothes untouched but wound the heart. You make men love the ugly and think it beautiful. Who gave you such power? Who gave you so unsuitable a name? If you were love indeed, you would love your servants. If they lived happily they would not kill themselves, as my beloved daughter has done.

What is the fate of your servants and ministers? The false pandar Celestina died at the hands of the most faithful servants she had ever recruited in your poisonous cause. They were beheaded, Calisto fell from the wall, and my beloved daughter chose to die the same death in order to follow him. You were the cause of all this. They have given you a sweet name, but you perform bitter deeds, and you do not give equal rewards. The law is wicked that is not fair to all. We rejoice at the sound of your name, but our dealings with you make us sad. Happy are those whom you have never known or never noticed. Some, induced by an error of the senses, have called you a god. But it is a strange god that kills its own children, as you kill your followers. In defiance of all reason, you give the richest gifts to those who serve you least, so that in the end you may draw them into your painful dance. You are an enemy to your friends, a friend to your enemies. Why do you act without rhyme or reason? They paint you as a poor blind boy, and put a bow in your hand with which you shoot at random; but it is your ministers that are blind, for they never feel or see how harsh is the reward you give to those who serve you. Your fire is a burning flash that leaves no mark where it strikes. Its flames are fed with the souls and lives of human beings, so numberless that if I tried to count them I do not know where I should begin. Not only of Christians, but of pagans and Jews; and all in requital for their worship of you. What would you say of Macias, who in our day died of love, and of whose sad end you were the cause? What did Paris do for you? And Helen? And Hypermnestra? And Aegisthus? Everyone knows the answer. What payment did you give to Sappho, Ariadne, and Leander? You would not leave even David and Solomon unharmed. And did not Samson pay the penalty for trusting her in whom you forced him to put his faith? There are many more whom I leave unmentioned, for my own evils are a sufficient theme.

I complain of the world because it created me in its bosom; because if it had not given me life I should not have fathered Melibea. If she had not been born I should not have loved her; if I had not loved I would cease to complain and my old age would not be desolate. O my daughter, my dear companion, dashed to pieces on the ground, why would you not let me prevent your death? Why did you not take pity on your darling mother, whom you loved? Why did you behave so cruelly to your old father? Why did you leave me in torment? Why did you leave me sad and alone in this vale of tears?

Some other translations by J. M. Cohen
in the Penguin Classics are
described on the
following pages

BERNAL DÍAZ

THE CONQUEST OF NEW SPAIN

Translated by J. M. Cohen

The defeat of the Aztecs by Hernan Cortes and his small band of adventurers is one of the most startling military feats in history. Fifty years after the event Bernal Díaz (*c.*1498 – *c.*1580), who served under Cortes, wrote this magnificent account of the march from the coast, Montezuma's death, the massacre of the Spaniards, and the eventual capture of the capital of Mexico.

This is a new translation of a work on which W. H. Prescott drew freely for his *History of the Conquest of Mexico*.

CERVANTES

DON QUIXOTE

Translated by J. M. Cohen

Don Quixote – by far the best-known book in Spanish literature – was originally intended by Cervantes as a skit on traditional popular ballads; but he also parodied the romances of chivalry. As a result he produced one of the most entertaining adventure stories of all time and created, in Don Quixote and his faithful squire, Sancho Panza, two of the greatest characters in fiction. By 1615, when he died, 'old, a soldier, a gentleman and poor,' his book was already famous in both French and English.

J. M. Cohen's translation presents a great work in lively, vigorous, and modern English.

RABELAIS

GARGANTUA AND PANTAGRUEL

Translated by J. M. Cohen

Gargantua and Pantagruel stands unique among the world's literature for its robust exuberance and monstrous exaggeration. Rabelais (*c.* 1494–1553), a monk who also qualified as a Bachelor of Medicine, was persecuted by both religious and civil authorities for its publication. As he chronicles the fantastic adventures of the two giants, a series of caricatures emerges, depicting the church hierarchy, schools and universities, theologians, lawyers, and philosophers. The impression received is of the conflict of two ages overlapping: the new age of humanism, research, and individualism, and the former one of the fixed world-order of the schoolmen.

MONTAIGNE

ESSAYS

Translated by J. M. Cohen

In his essays Michel de Montaigne (1533–92) penned a portrait of himself in a frame of timelessness. Following an entirely new, non-chronological method of autobiography, he set out to test his responses to situations and to ascertain the permanence of his impressions and opinions. Against a brilliant range of subjects – from cannibals to physiognomy – the man displayed is objectively detached, tireless in his search for truth, and at all times restrained. His essential modesty is revealed nowhere more clearly than in his famous medal with its inscription *Que sçais-je?*

ROUSSEAU

CONFESSIONS

Translated by J. M. Cohen

In his posthumously published *Confessions* Jean-Jacques Rousseau (1712–78) describes the first fifty-three years of his life. With a frankness at times almost disconcerting, but always refreshing, he set out to reveal the whole truth about himself to the world, and succeeded in producing a masterpiece which has left its indelible imprint on the literature of successive generations, influencing among others Proust, Goethe, and Tolstoy.

J. M. Cohen's translation provides a clear, easy rendering in contemporary English of this fascinating panorama of eighteenth-century continental life, which ranges freely from the *haut monde* to the picaresque.